GEM TRAILS

■ OF ■

NORTHERN CALIFORNIA

By James R. Mitchell

Gem Guides Book Co.
315 Cloverleaf Dr., Suite F
Baldwin Park, CA 91706

First Edition 1995
Second Edition 2005

Library of Congress Control Number: 2005927826
ISBN - 10: 1-889786-28-4
ISBN - 13: 978-1-889786-28-5

Maps: Janet Francisco, Jean Hammond & John Mayerski
Cover Art: Scott Roberts
Cover Photograph: Courtesy Robin Johnson, co-author *Geology Trails of Northern California*

NOTE:
   Due to the possibility of personal error, typographical error, misinterpretation of information, and the many changes due to man or nature, *Gem Trails of Northern California*, its publisher, and all other persons directly or indirectly associated with this publication, assume no responsibility for accidents, injury, or any losses by individuals or groups using this publication.
   In rough terrain and hazardous areas, all persons are advised to be aware of possible changes due to man or nature that occur along the gem trails.

TABLE OF CONTENTS

Site #   **Page #**
REGION I

Site		Page#

INTRODUCTION TO REVISED EDITION

As you look through this, the second edition of *Gem Trails Of Northern California*, you will notice that the maps have been improved, driving instruction enhanced and, within allowable space limitations, there are better collecting tips and mineral descriptions. There are some new locations to explore - and a few sites are no longer listed because they have been closed or thoroughly depleted.

A great challenge facing authors of collecting guidebooks such as the *Gem Trails* series is the volatility of so many of the locations. A spot where the ground was literally covered with mineral specimens 10 years ago, might have little or nothing left as a result of intense collecting over the years. Then comes a decision, should the site be left in the revised book or taken out. The author has attempted to provide a realistic accounting of not only what can be found at each site but, equally as important, how easy or difficult it is to get those minerals.

It is also important to convey to readers that a major reason some sites have been closed over the years is the result of a few irresponsible visitors either leaving trash or damaging property. It is a shame that everybody must pay the price for the actions (or inaction) of a very few. Fear of frivolous lawsuits was also listed as a reason many private property owners have decided to disallow collectors. Why should a kind property owner be forced to pay exorbitant liability insurance fees in order to be nice? Another reason some sites have been eliminated is increased governmental restrictions and land closures. The current politically correct thinking seems to be totally closing off sections of "public" land to everyone except those very few who are strong enough to get in and out by foot.

When people think of Northern California and minerals, visions of glittering gold usually come to mind... but there is so much more. There is jade, often occurring in qualities rivaling that from Wyoming or Burma; beautiful pink rhodonite, as fine as from anywhere; and possibly the most diverse variety of gem obsidian in the entire country, if not the world. The most reliable gold locations tend to be within the legendary Gold Rush Country, situated in the mountains east of Sacramento, and, within that scenic and historic region, weekend prospectors can still successfully pan for tiny nuggets and flakes.

The variety and quality of minerals is primarily due to the region's unique geological history. The Northern California topography is complex, ranging from mighty volcanic peaks to desolate deserts, with just about everything between. This diversity is largely the result of the ongoing collision of the "floating" North American continent with the more stationary ocean floor. The resulting crush has caused the land to "crumple", creating lofty mountain ranges and desolate lowlands. In addition, the immense heat and pressure generated by the continental collision is the primary contributor to the Cascade Volcano Chain, which still continues to alter the landscape.

There is igneous rock, as a result of the volcanic activity; metamorphic rock, formed from the intense pressure and heat of the continental collisions; and sedimentary rock, marking the locations of ancient seas and lakes.

Within the pages of this book are directions to places where you can find a good sampling of the minerals and fossils that Northern California has to offer. The locations are as full of variety as the minerals themselves. The terrain includes pine covered mountains, barren desert, and beautiful beaches. In addition, your journey will take you through spectacular scenery, countless historical sites, and numerous recreational facilities.

Northern California also boasts a number of sizable urban areas, including beautiful San Francisco, a metropolis affording boundless variety for visitors. And what a contrast it is to drive into such a place, after having spent a few days exploring remote collecting sites. Sacramento, the state's capitol, is also a suggested stop. This was a key transportation center during the gold rush era, and Old Town is a must visit for anyone interested in American mining history.

One can hardly conjure up images of California without having visions of beautiful, sandy beaches. The northern part of the state, though, doesn't have as much of the pristine white sands so prominent in the south. Most of the shoreline in the north is either rocky or covered with gravel. The scenery, however, is frequently rugged and spectacular, and many of those beaches offer great collecting potential. Amongst the gravel and other rock are often found pebbles of agate, jasper, fossils, and other minerals, and there is something very special about the experience of rockhounding on the shores of the mighty Pacific Ocean. The sea breeze, thunderous crashing waves, and the cooling ocean spray provide for a most unique collecting trip.

It is important to note that many of the maps accompanying the descriptions are intentionally **NOT DRAWN TO SCALE**. The purpose is to have one illustration providing not only the general location setting, but also detailed travel instructions near the site itself.

Some of the spots mentioned are on or near dumps of old and abandoned mines. <u>Do **not**</u>, under any circumstances, enter the shafts, and always be cautious when exploring the surrounding regions. There are often hidden tunnels, rotten ground, pits, rusty nails, broken glass and discarded chemicals, all of which create hazards.

A few of the sites are on private property and access is not guaranteed, or, possibly, a fee may be charged to collect there. Fee information and land status is discussed in the text as it was at time of publication, but **DO NOT ASSUME THAT THIS GUIDE GIVES PERMISSION TO COLLECT!** Land status changes frequently. If you have a suspicion that a particular site is no longer open, be sure to inquire locally.

Collectors are reminded of government regulations about collecting petrified wood. Rockhounds can obtain no more than 25 pounds of wood per day, plus one piece, and no more than 250 pounds per year. To acquire a specimen weighing more than 250 pounds, a permit must be procured from the District Manager of the Bureau of Land Management. Groups *cannot* pool their allocations together, and wood from public lands cannot be bartered or sold to commercial dealers, and may only be obtained with hand tools.

To further complicate matters, *some* National Forests have recently placed restrictions on the collection of fossils and obsidian within their boundaries. It would probably be wise to inquire at local Forest Service offices for updated details, suggestions, and/or permits.

Most of the areas discussed in the book are easy to get to, unless otherwise noted in the text, but road conditions do change. Severe weather can make good roads very rough, and very rough roads totally impassable, even with four-wheel drive. You must decide for yourself what your particular vehicle is capable of. Do not go where your car was not designed to go!! It is also imperative to point out that different vehicles' odometers might vary considerably in regard to measuring distances. Mileage may also have discrepancies due to wheel slippage on a dirt road or snow or ice. The mileage presented in this book is as accurate as the author could make it, but treat it more as a good approximation. Look for turnoffs before and after the mileage given in the text and remember that the greater the distance, the higher the probability that there may be some variance from car to car.

Be advised that northern California can get quite cold and wet during the winter months. In fact, many of the mountain passes are completely closed from late fall until late spring, so visits to those locations would be best planned for warmer periods. Also keep in mind that the desolate desert regions can be especially hazardous during the scorching summer months. Use good judgment as to where you go and when you go. When venturing into some of the more remote areas, it is a good idea to take extra drinking water, foul weather clothing, and even some food, just in case you get delayed or stuck.

There have been many changes to our hobby during the more than thirty-five years I have been a participant. Many of those changes, as you may have detected, have been frustrating and disappointing. The one thing, however, that has remained constant is that rockhounds and mineral collectors, as a group, tend to be a most friendly, helpful, sharing and congenial group of people. They have a true love for the outdoors and thoroughly enjoy "the hunt." They not only like to seek minerals, but they cherish friendships made while in the field and have just about as much fun sharing ideas and techniques as they do with the work itself. I am thankful that, in a small way, I have had a part in introducing so many people to this hobby.

James R. Mitchell

ROCKHOUND RULES

The following are a few basic rules that should always be followed no matter what state or country you are collecting in.

(1) Tell someone where you are going and what time you expect to return.

(2) Do not collect alone—have at least one companion with you.

(3) Wear appropriate clothing: long pants; work boots, preferably with steel toes; a hard hat if working around vertical rock faces; heavy work gloves; and protective eye wear if you are going to be hammering.

(4) Research the area you are going to—what kind of vehicle is needed to get there; what is to be found; are there old mine shafts you should be aware of or other dangers; and what kind of equipment will you need.

(5) Always ask permission to enter a property if possible.

(6) Leave all gates in the position that you found them.

(7) Do not disturb livestock.

(8) Never, ever litter. If possible, leave the place cleaner than it was when you arrived.

(9) Do not "hog" the site or make it difficult for the next person to collect.

(10) Do not leave children or pets unattended. They can get into serious trouble.

(11) Never leave fires unattended, and do not light them in dry, hazardous conditions.

(12) Bring a first aid kit with you and know how to use it in case someone is in need of medical attention.

(13) Never enter abandoned mines without proper training, equipment and permission—and never alone.

Enjoy your collecting and the wonderful hobby that we all share. Be safe, obey the laws. Always be considerate and we will have a hobby for many years to come. Remember, all it takes is one thoughtless person to close down a collecting locality.

HINTS FOR COLLECTING MINERALS

Following are some suggestions for collecting minerals:

(1) Necessary items are a prospector's pick, safety goggles, gloves, wrapping materials, hand lens, notebook, pen and hand rake. Your equipment should also include items from the following categories and possibly some of these options.

- *Shovels:*   collapsible shovel, spade, miner's shovel
- *Large Picks:*   miner's pick, 16-inch ore pick
- *Striking Tools:* crack hammer, chisel point pick, maul
- *Chisels:*   cold chisel, wedge, gad, screwdriver
- *Options:*   hydraulic jack, augers, hand drill, bent wire

(2) When working in a mine dump look for any mineral which is different from the rest of the pile in color, translucency, shape, luster or texture.

(3) Look for specimens which are combinations of several minerals.

(4) Work with someone. When there is heavy digging or rock moving, alternate jobs.

(5) Look for cavities in the rock walls.

(6) Split large rocks which are composed of several minerals.

(7) Look for a contact zone, an area where two different types of rock meet.

(8) Micromounts are found in small seams, vugs, old natural fractures, between mica and feldspar plates and in loose coarse material. Examine all specimens with suspected micromount qualities with a 10-power hand lens.

(9) If you find a good specimen, try to trace where it came from.

(10) If you are in a mine or quarry, identify the principal rocks, know what minerals may be found with them, and seek out any layer which shows the characteristics you are looking for. Prospect several areas quickly before selecting a place to dig.

(11) A water bottle with sprayer is handy on old mine dumps.

(12) Investigate the ground around old dumps and old mines.

Excerpted from Midwest Gem, Fossil, and Mineral Trails: Prairie States, *by June Culp Zeitner.*

HINTS FOR COLLECTING GEM MATERIALS

Following are some suggestions for collecting gem materials:

(1) Walk back and forth looking at the rocks with the sun in front of you and then behind you. Agates and chalcedony are translucent with the light shining through them. Patterns show off better with the sun behind you.

(2) Look for gemstones after rains, if possible. Moisture makes the patterns and color stand out.

(3) Learn to check rocks in the field. A small chip can be knocked off from the edge with a prospector's pick. Holding the rock firmly with one hand and strike it quickly at the edge with a hard blow. Let your wrist give with the blow.

(4) If a rock is already broken, a conchoidal fracture is often a sign it is polishable.

(5) Look in streams and along lakes, and also on the grassy hillsides and dirt banks along the lakes and streams.

(6) If a rock is of good color but badly fractured, remember your tumbler.

(7) Agates may have oxidized coatings. They may also have thumbprint depressions or pockmarks.

(8) Make a record on the spot of any find you make which is strange or unusual in any way.

(9) A spray bottle of water will help determine the characteristics of individual gem materials.

Excerpted from Midwest Gem, Fossil, and Mineral Trails: Prairie States, *by June Culp Zeitner.*

BUREAU OF LAND MANAGEMENT
Street: 1620 L Street NW
Washington, DC 20036
Mailing: 1849 C Street NW
Washington, DC 20240
www.blm.gov

CALIFORNIA BLM STATE OFFICE
2800 Cottage Way, Suite W 1834
Sacramento, CA 95825-1886
(916) 978-4400

USDA FOREST SERVICE
P.O.Box 96090
Washington, DC 20090-6090
(202) 720-USDA

US GEOLOGICAL SURVEY
(888) ASK-USGS (275-8747)
www.usgs.gov

US GEOLOGICAL SURVEY
WESTERN REGION
345 Middlefield Road
Menlo Park, CA 94025
(650) 853-8300

US GEOLOGICAL SURVEY
CENTRAL REGION
Box 25046
Denver Federal Center
Denver, CO 80225
(303) 236-5900

CALIFORNIA GEOLOGICAL SURVEY
801 K Street, MS 12-30
Sacramento, CA 95814
(916) 445-1825
(916) 445-5718 Fax
cgshq@consrv.ca.gov
http://www.consrv.ca.gov/CGS/

ROCK AND MINERAL SOCIETIES

**AMADOR COUNTY GEM &
MINERAL SOCIETY**
P.O. Box 794
Sutter Creek, CA 95685

**CALAVERAS GEM & MINERAL
SOCIETY**
P.O. Box 517
Angels Camp, CA 95222-0517

**CONTRA COSTA MINERAL & GEM
CLUB**
P.O. Box 4667
Walnut Creek, CA 94596-4667

**EL DORADO COUNTY MINERAL &
GEM SOCIETY**
P.O. Box 950
Placerville, CA 95667-0950
www.eldoradomineralandgem.org

MARIPOSA GEM & MINERAL CLUB
P.O. Box 753
Mariposa, CA 95338-0753

**MOTHER LODE MINERAL
SOCIETY**
P.O. Box 1263
Modesto, CA 95353

**NEVADA COUNTY GEM &
MINERAL SOCIETY**
P.O. Box 565
Nevada City, CA 95959-0565

**NORTHERN CALIFORNIA
MINERALOGICAL ASSOCIATION**
8065 Silverleaf Way
Sacramento, CA 95821

**SACRAMENTO MINERAL
SOCIETY**
P.O. Box 160544
Sacramento, CA 95816-0544

**SAN FRANCISCO GEM &
MINERAL SOCIETY**
4134 Judah Street
San Francisco, CA 94122

**SEQUOIA GEM & MINERAL
SOCIETY**
P.O. Box 1245
Redwood City, CA 94064-1245

**SHASTA GEM & MINERAL
SOCIETY**
P.O. Box 424
Redding, CA 96099

CALIFORNIA STATE MINING & MINERAL MUSEUM
5005 Fairgrounds Road
P.O.Box 1192
Mariposa, CA 95338
(209) 742-7625

EMPIRE MINE STATE HISTORIC PARK
10791 E. Empire Street
Grass Valley, CA 95945
(530) 273-8522

GOLD COUNTRY MUSEUM
1273 High Street
Auburn, CA 95603
(530) 889-6500

KENTUCKY MINE PARK AND MUSEUM
1050 South Maine Street
Sierra City, CA 96125
(530) 862-1310
(775) 423-3662 Fax

MALAKOFF DIGGINS STATE HISTORIC PARK
23579 Blue Field Road
Nevada City, CA 95959
(530) 265-2740

NEW ALMADEN QUICKSILVER MINING MUSEUM
21350 Almaden Road
Historic New Almaden, CA 95120
(408) 323-1107

PLACER COUNTY MUSEUM
101 Maple Street
Auburn, CA 95603
(530) 889-6500

SUTTER GOLD MINE
13660 Highway 49
Sutter Creek, CA 95685
(209) 267-5594

MAP LEGEND

——⬡80———	Interstate Highway
——⬭95———	U.S. Highway
——(140)———	State Highway
——| 81 |———	Highway/Local/Forest Road
———————	Road/Street/Avenue
═══════════	Maintained Dirt Road
==========	Unmaintained Dirt Road
- - - - - - -	Trail
✖	Collecting Area

KEY SITES TO LOCATOR MAP

Site No.

REGION I

(1) Happy Camp
(2) Slater Butte
(3) Jenny Creek
(4) Etna
(5) Mt. Shasta
(6) Ashland
(7) Lassen Creek
(8) Fandango Pass
(9) Sugar Hill
(10) Davis Creek
(11) Cedarville
(12) Deep Creek
(13) Northwest Nevada
(14) Granger Creek
(15) Patrick's Point
(16) Willow Creek
(17) Coffee Creek
(18) Weaverville
(19) Douglas City
(20) Hayfork
(21) Big Flat
(22) Van Duzen River
(23) Ruth
(24) Butte Creek
(25) Belden
(26) Jacks Valley
(27) Susanville
(28) Alderpoint
(29) Kettenpom

REGION II

(30) Covelo
(31) Mina
(32) Hearst
(33) Stony Creek
(34) Highway 70
(35) Pulga
(36) Serpentine Canyon
(37) La Porte
(38) Gold Valley
(39) Goodyear's Bar
(40) Babcock Peak
(41) Taylorsville
(42) Hallelujah Mountain
(43) Kelseyville
(44) Clear Lake

Site No.

REGION II (continued)

(45) California Petrified Forest
(46) Chalk Bluff
(47) Crystal Peak
(48) Union Flat
(49) Virginia City Fossils
(50) Gold Rush Country North

REGION III

(51) Traverse Creek
(52) Folsom Lake
(53) Gold Rush Country South
(54) Bear River
(55) Mt. Reba
(56) Valley Springs
(57) Bridgeport
(58) Dillon Beach & Point Reyes
(59) Bolinas
(60) Pacifica South
(61) Patterson
(62) Anderson Lake
(63) Coulterville
(64) Aeolian Buttes
(65) Obsidian Dome
(66) Basalt Jasper
(67) Fish Lake Valley

REGION IV

(68) Big Pine
(69) Eureka Valley
(70) Hanging Rock Canyon
(71) Westgard Pass
(72) Owens Valley
(73) Mazourka Canyon
(74) Lone Pine
(75) Cottonwood Lakes
(76) Jade Cove

NORTHERN CALIFORNIA SITE MAP

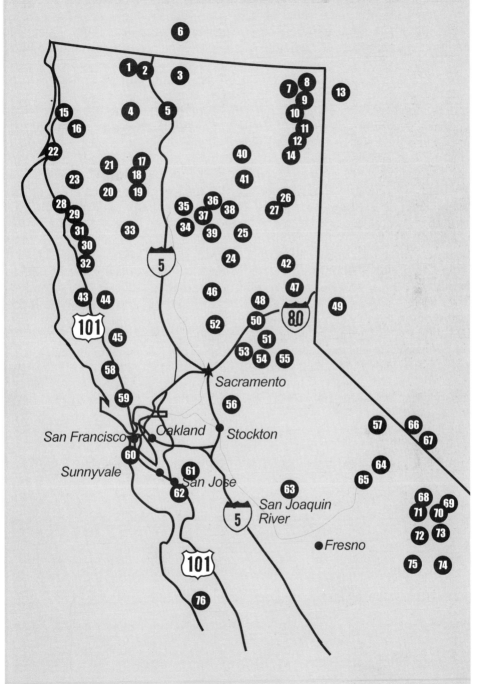

HAPPY CAMP

Serpentine and jade, some of very good quality, highlight what can be found in and around many of the streams and rivers near Happy Camp. In addition, a good grade of rhodonite can be picked up, as can bowenite nodules and crystals of idocrase, garnet and pyrite. Probably the best collecting is at Site "A", which, at one time, was a private claim, but, according to local sources, amateur collectors are still allowed to gather specimens. As with all claims, however, it is essential that you properly determine the status when you visit. The final two-tenths of a mile leading to the river's edge and Site "A" is blocked by a log to prevent driving into the water. Just park in the wide clearing and walk that remaining short distance.

The jade and serpentine are fairly easy to spot, due to their green color. This is especially true for specimens in the shallow creek which are continuously being cleaned by the running water. The rhodonite is far more difficult to find, since it is usually covered with an unappealing black crust. Due to that "camouflage", be sure to split any suspect black stones in hopes of exposing beautiful pink interiors. Walk a distance, in either direction, alongside the stream. Carefully examine stones in the creek, as well as alongside its banks. Needless to say, one advantage to collecting next to a stream is the convenient accessibility of water for washing specimens. Anything found on the bank can easily be rinsed to aid in identification. If you are dissatisfied with what can be found on the surface, digging may expose additional specimens.

Site "B", on the west branch of Indian Creek, offers similar material in smaller amounts. In fact, just about any of the creeks in the region offer potentially productive collecting. Just be sure not to trespass onto private property without first getting permission.

Parked at Happy Camp, Site A

HAPPY CAMP

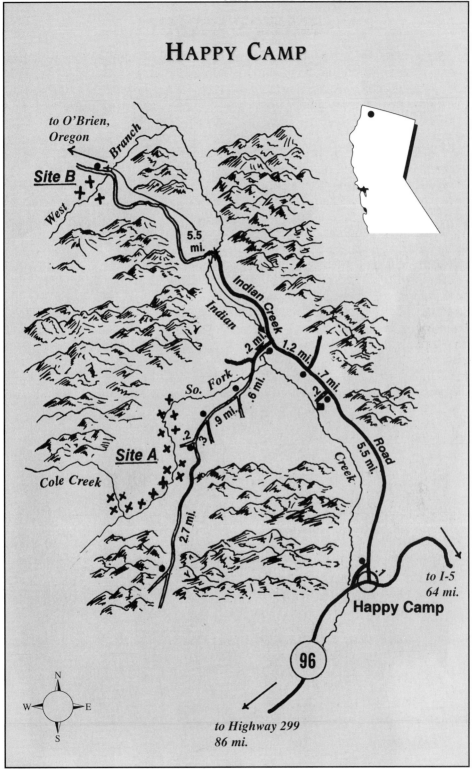

to O'Brien,
Oregon

Branch

Site B

West

5.5
mi.

Indian

Indian Creek

.2 mi.

1.2 mi.

.7 mi.

So. Fork

.6 mi.

.9 mi.

.2

.3

Site A

Cole Creek

2.7 mi.

Road
5.5
mi.

Creek

.1

to I-5
64 mi.

Happy Camp

96

N
W — E
S

to Highway 299
86 mi.

SLATER BUTTE

Serpentine and occasional pieces of jade can be found in the abandoned quarry designated as Site "A" on the accompanying map. As is the case with any mine and quarry, be certain to collect in safe locations, be on the lookout for hidden pits, and under no circumstances, enter a shaft.

The minerals are fairly easy to obtain by digging through the rubble. The telltale green color of the serpentine and jade make those minerals fairly easy to spot, since their vivid hues stand out against the lighter colored soil. Pieces range in size from tiny chips and pebbles to large boulders, and the quality also has a considerably wide range. Everything from highly splintered and poorly colored chunks to those exhibiting nice, solid greens. Much of the serpentine will take a polish, and material with random black and/or white areas are especially desirable. The jade, for the most part, is not of high quality, being somewhat pale, but a few worthwhile pieces can usually be found, with patience. Remember that the collecting status of old mines changes from time to time, so if there are any indications that the quarry has been reactivated, be sure to inquire before digging.

Site "B" offers an additional opportunity to gather more jade and serpentine. The material here tends to be less fractured than that from Site "A", thereby being slightly more desirable for cutting and polishing. It is far more difficult to find specimens at Site "B", however, since the region is covered with thick brush and trees. Collectors must first find a good place to pull off the road, since other motorists will not be expecting to encounter a parked car. It is then necessary to carefully climb on the hillsides to find the minerals. It isn't an especially hazardous place to explore, but, if not careful, one could easily slip. Do not go onto any terrain that may be more rugged than you are capable of hiking through!

Collecting just off the road at Slater Butte, Site B

SLATER BUTTE

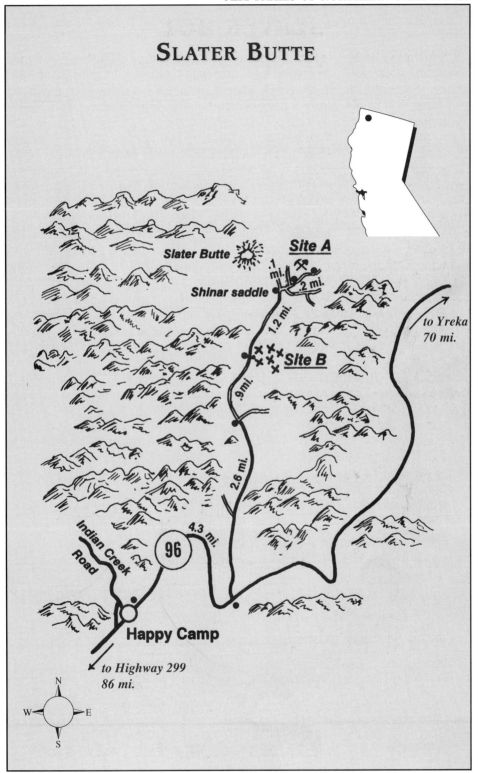

Slater Butte

Shinar saddle

Site A

Site B

.1 mi.

.2 mi.

1.2 mi.

.9 mi.

2.6 mi.

4.3 mi.

96

Indian Creek Road

Happy Camp

to Yreka 70 mi.

to Highway 299 86 mi.

N
W E
S

JENNY CREEK

Jasper, rhodonite, carnelian, agate, and petrified wood can all be found along Jenny Creek, just north of the Iron Gate Reservoir. The best collecting starts from where the creek passes near the Wilkes Expedition Memorial and continues for at least one and one-half miles north, as illustrated on the accompanying map. Search on both sides of the road, paying particularly close attention to the streambed, the soft soil on its banks, and any other adjacent areas of erosion. You should also examine the roadbed and berm, especially if freshly graded or after a recent rainstorm. It is easy to spot the gemstones, since their bright colors stand out vividly against the soil.

Nothing is overly plentiful, but brightly colored jasper is the most frequently encountered of the Jenny Creek minerals. It is of high quality and comes in many colors, including red, yellow, rust and orange. Agate is generally found in darker shades, with some containing interesting inclusions. Occasional chunks of beautiful orange carnelian can also be acquired, but these are rare. It takes some real patience and perseverance to gather worthwhile quantities but, if you have the time, you should be rewarded. The rhodonite is equally difficult to obtain, not as much because of its scarcity, but due to the black crust coating most pieces. It is generally necessary to use a rock pick and split any suspect stones in hopes of exposing a prized pink interior. The rhodonite occurs in a range of qualities, from a near black to a brilliant pink. As you might expect, the latter is the most scarce. Rockhounds can also pick up occasional pieces of brown and tan petrified wood.

In spite of the fact that nothing at Jenny Creek is overly abundant, the variety and quality helps to make up for that deficiency. If you have the time, be sure to also explore some of the other nearby creeks and roads. This entire region boasts nice cutting materials and you may just happen upon something very nice.

Searching through the river rock at Jenny Creek

JENNY CREEK

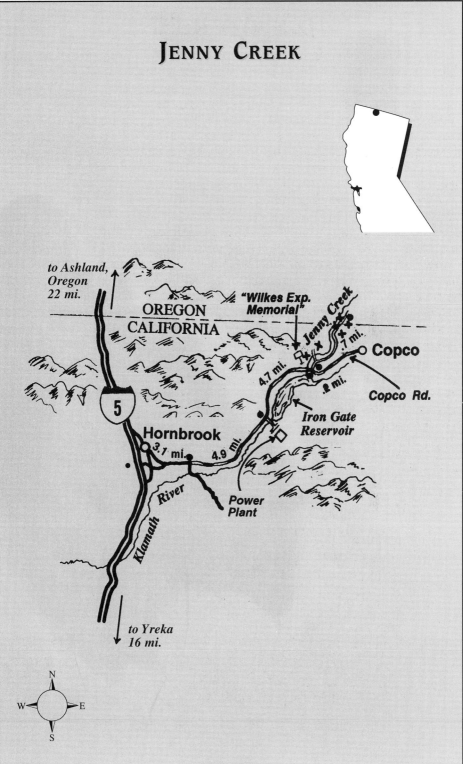

to Ashland,
Oregon
22 mi.

OREGON
CALIFORNIA

"Wilkes Exp.
Memorial"

Jenny Creek

Copco

.7 mi.

4.7 mi.

.8 mi.

Copco Rd.

Iron Gate
Reservoir

Hornbrook

3.7 mi.   4.9 mi.

Klamath River

Power
Plant

5

to Yreka
16 mi.

N
W — E
S

ETNA

This location offers collectors the opportunity to gather a good, solid variety of marble which can be used to produce larger polished pieces, including bookends, clock faces and carvings. To get to this roadside locality, from Etna, simply follow the signs toward Sawyers Bar. The deposit is easy to spot, being just off the pavement. The blocky, white marble stands out alongside the road, making it difficult to miss.

Most of what can be found here is white, thereby not being overly desirable. Some, however, displays a beautiful light pink and/or green hue, that being what most collectors are looking for. In fact, single chunks exhibiting white, pink and green together can be used to make extraordinary polished pieces.

It is mandatory that you park well off the pavement, since other drivers will not be expecting a stopped car in this locality. Good specimens can be found by carefully searching through the loose rocks or by directly attacking the outcrop itself with gads, chisels, and a sledge hammer. Most collectors have found that fine specimens can be obtained from within the rubble at the base of the deposit, making the sledge hammer work unnecessary. That, however, is up to you.

Do not allow stones onto the pavement. If you choose to attack the deposit with hard rock tools, don't work under overhangs, since you may loosen a large boulder from above.

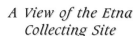

A View of the Etna Collecting Site

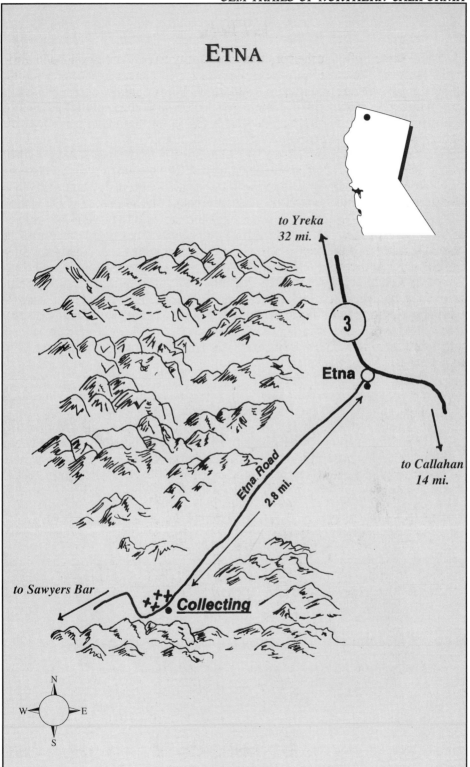

ETNA

to Yreka
32 mi.

3

Etna

to Callahan
14 mi.

Etna Road

2.8 mi.

to Sawyers Bar

Collecting

N
W   E
S

MOUNT SHASTA

This site is situated in the shadow of spectacular Mt. Shasta, helping to make it one of the most scenic rockhounding areas in California. The collecting is done in and around the dumps of an old copper mine where rockhounds can gather fine specimens of metallic chalcocite and chalcopyrite, as well as colorful malachite and chrysocolla. The prospect is difficult to spot from the main road, but, as you turn onto the ruts leading into the area, the dumps will be seen through the trees.

The green and blue malachite and chrysocolla are easy to find, due to their bright colors, but that isn't the case for the far more elusive chalcocite and chalcopyrite. To find those minerals, it is usually necessary to split suspect rocks with a sledge hammer or other hard rock tools. When you do break up a mineral bearing stone, however, there will be no doubt whether or not it is a good specimen. If filled with crystals, they will sparkle in the sunlight. Much of the crystallization is exquisite, but not very large. Pieces containing lots of the chalcocite and chalcopyrite are, obviously, the best and can be used as fantastic display pieces for a mineral collection. Most of the malachite and chrysocolla is too porous and thin to polish, but can be used as eye catching display pieces.

If you are not satisfied with what can be found on the surface, try your luck at digging into the soft soil of the dumps. This generally produces better specimens, since the surface is quite picked over. It also, obviously, involves considerably more work. This mine has been abandoned for years, but if you suspect that status may have changed, be certain to ascertain if collecting is allowed before you pick up any minerals. Be very careful when exploring this or any abandoned mine. There are rusty nails, caustic chemicals, broken glass, potentially hidden pits, and unsafe shafts. For those reasons, be careful where you choose to park your car since this wouldn't be a great place to get a flat tire.

Searching old copper mine dumps at Mount Shasta Site

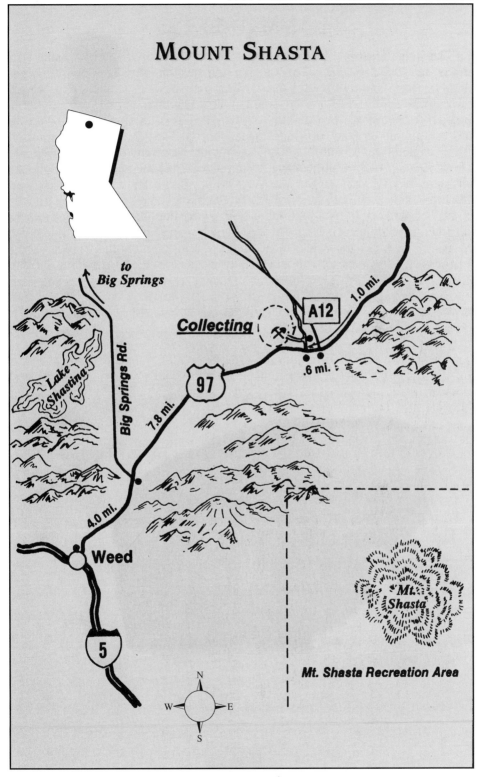

MOUNT SHASTA

to
Big Springs

Collecting

A12

1.0 mi.

Lake
Shastina

Big Springs Rd.

97

.6 mi.

7.8 mi.

4.0 mi.

Weed

5

Mt.
Shasta

Mt. Shasta Recreation Area

N
W   E
S

ASHLAND

The region east of Ashland, only a few miles north of the California border, in Oregon, provides collectors with fine specimens of agate and an occasional geode. One of the best places to find such minerals is about seven miles east of Interstate 5. To get there simply follow Highway 66 until dark basalt is spotted in the road cuts, primarily on the left side of the pavement. This outcrop continues at least four miles past milepost 9, and virtually any portion provides potential for finding agate and small crystal lined geodes. The agate is a secondary mineral here, easy to spot since it is much lighter in color than the host basalt. Some of the seams are wider and offer more potential than others, so take a little time to ascertain which might be best.

It is necessary to use gads and a sledge hammer to free the agate from its place within the tough basalt. Be careful while working that nothing is allowed to fall onto the pavement. It is recommended, after determining where the best agate seams are located, to move onto the upper basalt regions for easier and less hazardous working conditions.

Another good place to find some agate is nearby Emigrant Lake. You should be able to pick up little agate pebbles, especially if the water is low. Simply walk along the shore, keeping an eye out for some nice tumbling material.

Fossils can also be found in many of the road cuts near Ashland. It might be worthwhile, if you see one that looks especially promising, to stop and investigate. Some of the Ashland fossils are interesting and make great display pieces.

Parked alongside Highway 66 near the Ashland agate bearing basalt

ASHLAND

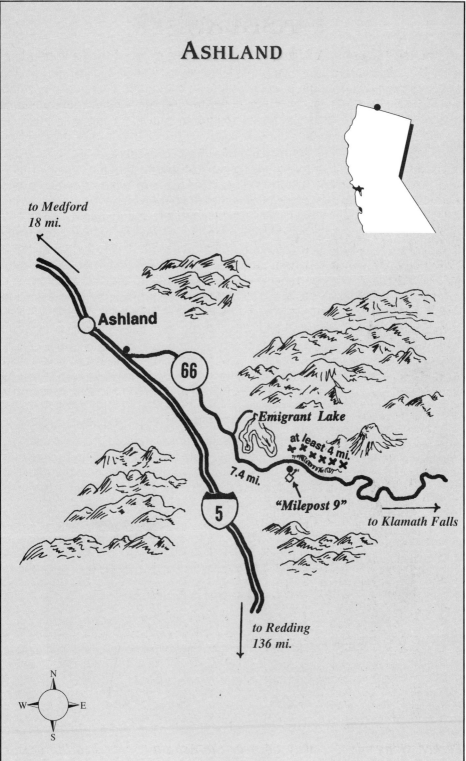

to Medford
18 mi.

Ashland

66

Emigrant Lake

at least 4 mi.

7.4 mi.

5

"Milepost 9"

to Klamath Falls

to Redding
136 mi.

N
W   E
S

LASSEN CREEK

The two sites illustrated on the accompanying map provide rockhounds with nice specimens of top quality obsidian. To get to Site A, start in the small town of Davis Creek, situated on Highway 395 about 20 miles north of Alturas. From Davis Creek, continue north along Highway 395 another 4 miles and then bear right onto the paved road generally paralleling the highway. Continue 4.4 miles to where a graded dirt road intersects from the east. Turn onto that road and drive 2.4 miles to Site A.

When you reach the given mileage, pull off the road at a convenient place and just start exploring. The prized volcanic glass is relatively easy to spot since the jet-black color stands out against the lighter colored soil, even when partially covered with pine needles. Pay particularly close attention to the hill just south of the road for sheen obsidian. Size tends to be small but a few boulders can be found hidden among the pine needles.

After visiting Site A, drive another 0.6 miles to the bridge crossing Lassen Creek and, from there continue at least 1 more mile to Site "B" where collectors can find even more obsidian, some of which is of faceting grade. You will see numerous weathered pits where previous collectors have been digging for beautiful golden, green, blue and silver sheen obsidian, as well as rainbow, black and mahogany varieties, all of which have made this particular spot so renown. Tons of material can be picked up from the surface, and, if you want to do some digging, nearly every boulder you encounter will be worth inspecting. The pick and shovel work is relatively easy since the soil is soft, but be sure to wear goggles and gloves since sharp splinters can be sent flying through the air if you strike a chunk of the volcanic glass in the wrong way.

Be advised that certain portions of the Modoc National Forest have restrictions on the amount of obsidian that any individual can pick up in a year. In fact, permits *may* be required. There is no fee for those permits to amateur collectors and they can be obtained at Forest Service offices in Alturas or Cedarville.

Lassen Creek site B

LASSEN CREEK

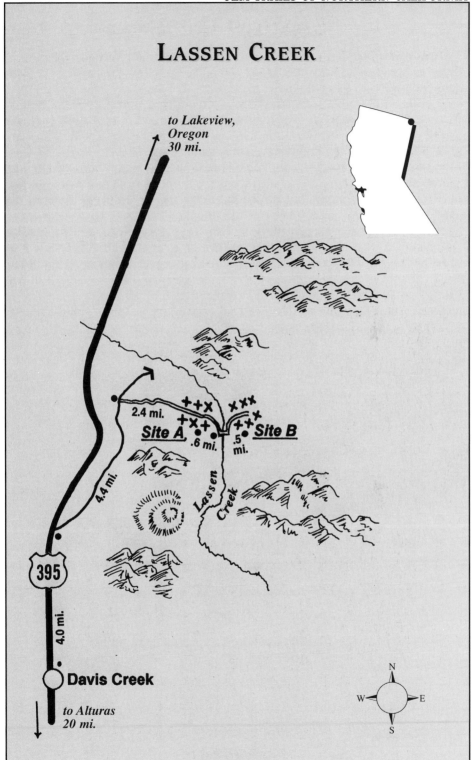

to Lakeview,
Oregon
30 mi.

2.4 mi.

+ + x   x x x

Site A   + x +   + x   **Site B**
        .6 mi.   .5
                 mi.

4.4 mi.

Lassen Creek

395

4.0 mi.

Davis Creek

to Alturas
20 mi.

N
W   E
S

FANDANGO PASS

Gem grade obsidian and small pieces of interesting petrified wood can be found at these two locations. To get to the first, follow Highway 395 north from Davis Creek approximately 13.5 miles to Fandango Pass Road where you should turn right. Travel east and then south 4 miles, as illustrated on the accompanying map, and then go right onto the dirt road. Follow that well graded road 0.75 miles and, from there, continuing at least 1 more mile, park anywhere and search in any direction, this being Site A. As is the case throughout this region, the black obsidian is easy to spot against the lighter colored soil. Since there is so much to be found here, take some time to find the best. Much is opaque, but prized faceting grade translucent material can also be gathered.

Site B is reached by returning to Fandango Pass Road and proceeding southeast 5.2 miles to where a little road can be seen on the right. Follow it up to 1.5 miles, parking just about anywhere starting at Fandango Pass Road. Rockhounds can pick up additional obsidian and even some specimens of petrified wood scattered throughout this region. Site B is not as prolific as Site A, but it encompasses a vast area. The farther you are willing to hike from the road to inspect the less accessible regions, the greater your chances will be for finding larger and better quality material.

The National Forest Service has enacted some restrictions on the amount of obsidian an individual can pick up each year and a permit might be required. Amateur collectors are not charged a fee for the permit and it would be wise to stop at the Forest Service office in either Alturas or Cedarville to obtain current regulations and restrictions, if there are any.

FANDANGO PASS

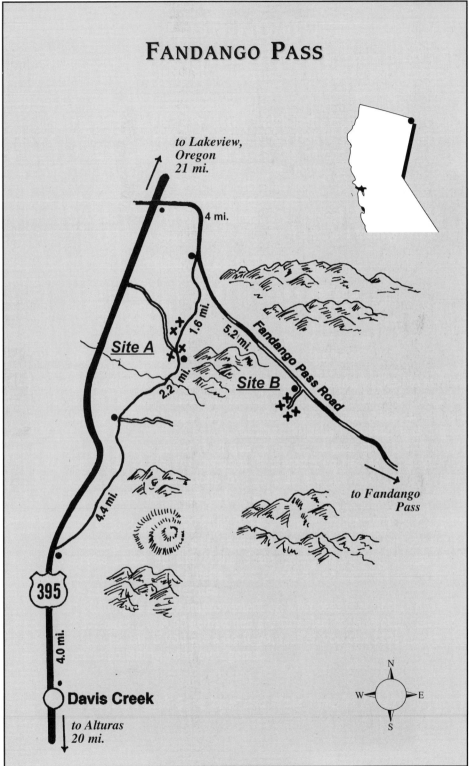

to Lakeview,
Oregon
21 mi.

4 mi.

1.6 mi.

5.2 mi.

Site A

Fandango Pass Road

2.2 mi.

Site B

to Fandango
Pass

4.4 mi.

395

4.0 mi.

⬤ **Davis Creek**

to Alturas
20 mi.

N
W — E
S

SUGAR HILL

The region surrounding Sugar Hill is arguably one of the best places in the country to find gem grade obsidian. To get to three of the finest Sugar Hill locations, start in the small town of Davis Creek. From the center of town, take the paved road leading to the cemetery, then into the forest, where it becomes well-graded dirt. From the cemetery, continue on the main road 4.1 miles and then make a hairpin right turn going another 2.2 miles to the intersection, as illustrated on the accompanying map.

Site A encompasses the intersection and the hillsides on either side of the road leading to the southeast. Collecting takes place within some dense and mountainous terrain, but, if careful, the somewhat challenging topography should present only minimal difficulty. Most of the obsidian found here is black, but pleasing brown and even mahogany specimens can be picked up. The quality and size vary considerably, with most of the gem material being somewhat small.

Site B is famous Obsidian Needle Hill, probably best known of all the region's locations. To get there, continue only 0.6 miles farther down the road and examine the large obsidian deposits on the hill to the right. Glassy needles cover that slope and it takes minimal effort to gather hundreds of them in a matter of minutes. In addition, one can find large chunks of beautiful double flow brown and black volcanic glass displaying fascinating spotted and swirled patterns. Most of what is found here is top quality and the quantity is unbelievable. Site C boasts even more obsidian, including a nice iris variety and it is reached by returning to the main Davis Creek road and going north 3.5 miles to the intersection depicted on the map.

While working at these sites, always keep in mind that obsidian is volcanic glass and shatters easily. Because of that, collectors are strongly advised to wear goggles, especially if they plan to split anything. It should also be noted that some parts of the Modoc National Forest are restricted in regard to the amount of obsidian that can be picked up by amateur collectors in any year. Permits may be required, but there is no fee involved. Further information and permits, if necessary, can be obtained at Forest Service offices in Alturas or Cedarville.

Searching Obsidian Hill

SUGAR HILL

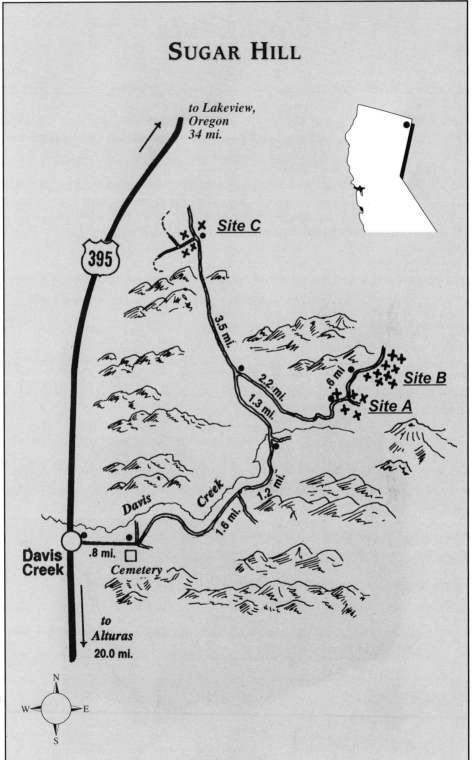

to Lakeview,
Oregon
34 mi.

395

× Site C

3.5 mi.

2.2 mi.

1.3 mi.

.6 mi.

++ Site B

Site A

Davis   Creek

1.2 mi.

1.6 mi.

**Davis
Creek**

.8 mi.

☐
Cemetery

to
Alturas
20.0 mi.

N
W   E
S

DAVIS CREEK

Here are three more Davis Creek obsidian locations which serve to further enhance the already stellar reputation this part of California has in regard to supplying quality volcanic glass. The material is so plentiful on the surface that you probably won't need any digging equipment. Be advised, however, if you do choose to dig into the relatively soft soil that obsidian shatters easily when struck with a hammer, pick or shovel. Because of that potential hazard, collectors are strongly advised to wear goggles and gloves when doing any excavation or splitting of samples.

To get to Site A, start in Davis Creek and take the paved road leading east from Highway 395 to the cemetery. Just past the cemetery, the road turns to well-graded dirt and that marks the start of Site A, an extensive region consisting of obsidian covered flatlands as far as the eye can see. Most is black, but some is a pleasing brown. The quality and size varies considerably, with most of the gem material being somewhat small. Simply park anywhere from pavement's end continuing at least 1 mile and explore in any direction.

Site B is reached by proceeding 2.8 miles from the cemetery and then turning right, driving another 1.4 miles. At Site B, you must hike up a steep trail to the main diggings where beautiful rainbow obsidian can be obtained. The trail, situated on the left side of the road, is somewhat difficult to spot due to the heavy ground-cover, but rubble from the diggings farther up the slope will help you find your way.

Fascinating obsidian needles can be gathered at Site C, a roadcut about 5 miles north of Davis Creek, alongside Highway 395. If you choose to explore this deposit, be *very* careful to park well off the pavement, do not get any rock on the highway, and watch out for high speed traffic.

Portions of the Modoc National Forest are restricted in regard to the amount of obsidian that can be picked up by amateur collectors in any year. Further information and permits, if necessary, can be obtained at Forest Service offices in Alturas or Cedarville.

Davis Creek Obsidian

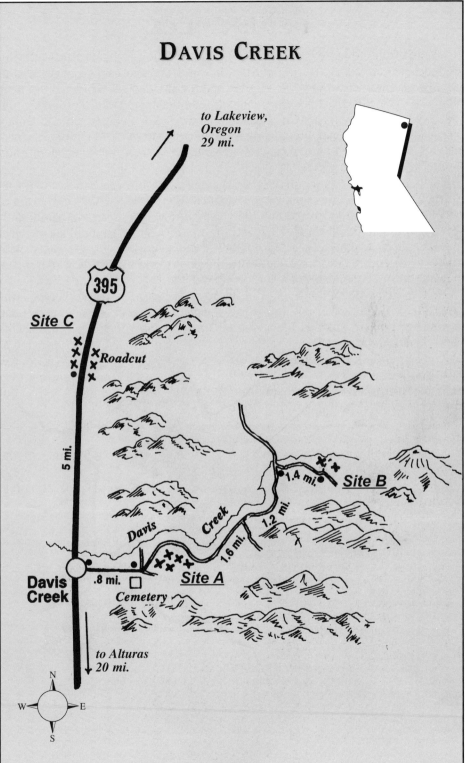

DAVIS CREEK

to Lakeview,
Oregon
29 mi.

395

Site C

Roadcut

5 mi.

Davis Creek

1.4 mi. Site B

1.2 mi.

1.6 mi.

Davis
Creek

.8 mi. Site A

Cemetery

to Alturas
20 mi.

N
W E
S

CEDARVILLE

This location provides collectors with agate and occasional pieces of interesting petrified wood. To get there, either go 18 miles east from Alturas or 5 miles west from Cedarville to the rough dirt road leading south from Highway 299. Go 0.1 miles, turn left, proceed 1.2 miles, and then go right to the creek. Be advised that these roads are somewhat washed out and can be especially treacherous if wet. This is especially true in regard to the route down to and across Cedar Creek. If you are not sure your vehicle is capable of navigating the road, simply find a place to pull off and hike from wherever you park. Keep in mind that this is a most remote place to get stuck. A further incentive to hike is that lots of fine agate and petrified wood can be found alongside the road scattered randomly throughout the entire region.

The primary collecting starts at the creek and continues for at least a half-mile in any direction. Since this is a densely forested area, leaves and pine needles often cover rocks lying on the ground. To deal with that problem, a garden rake is sometimes useful for exposing otherwise hidden minerals. You obviously can't rake the entire forest, but clearing especially promising areas might prove fruitful. In addition, pay particularly close attention to regions of erosion such as the creek banks. Not only does the running creek water continually expose fresh material, it can also be used to clean rocks for determining their desirability.

This entire region is most beautiful but be advised that it is primarily a summer site, often inaccessible during the winter due to snow.

Cedarville Area

CEDARVILLE

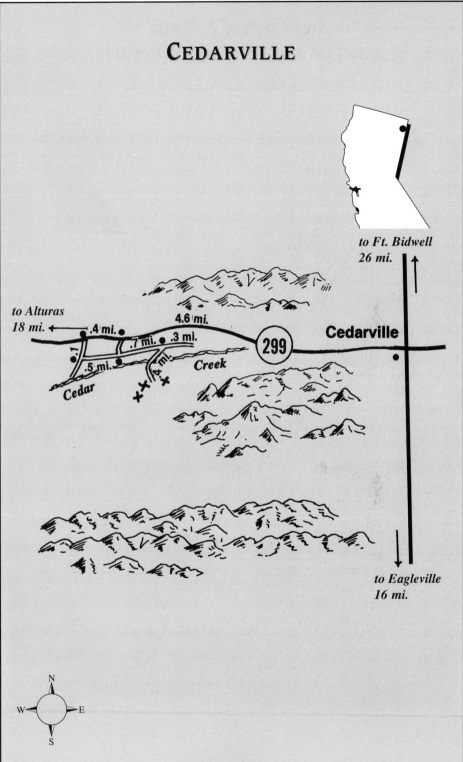

to Ft. Bidwell
26 mi.

to Alturas
18 mi.

4.6 mi.

.4 mi.

.7 mi.

.3 mi.

.1

.5 mi.

.2 mi.

Cedar

Creek

299

Cedarville

to Eagleville
16 mi.

N
W   E
S

DEEP CREEK

This collecting site provides collectors with both agate and petrified wood. To get there, start in Cedarville and head south 1.6 miles toward Eagleville. The unpaved road to the collecting site intersects from the west, just south of the cemetery and immediately before the bridge crossing North Deep Creek. Follow that road for 3.6 miles and park.

The agate and petrified wood is randomly scattered on both sides of the ruts leading up the hill to the north. Do not attempt driving on those ruts, however, since they are severely washed out. Material is most easily found in the relatively clear areas on and immediately adjacent to the eroded tracks, but the entire hillside offers good collecting potential. Since pine needles cover much of the ground, a small rake might be useful for exposing underlying rocks. The agate is generally white and clear with some containing nice bands and inclusions. Most have an orange crust, however, so any suspicious stones should be split to determine their true identity. Contorted chunks of agate can also be found here, and these make interesting display pieces without being polished. Nothing is overly concentrated, and most of what you find will be relatively small, suitable primarily for tumbling and making smaller cabochons. Be patient, though, and you should be able to gather worthwhile quantities in a relatively short amount of time.

This is primarily a summer site, since the ground is frequently covered with snow during other times of the year.

Collecting at Deep Creek

DEEP CREEK

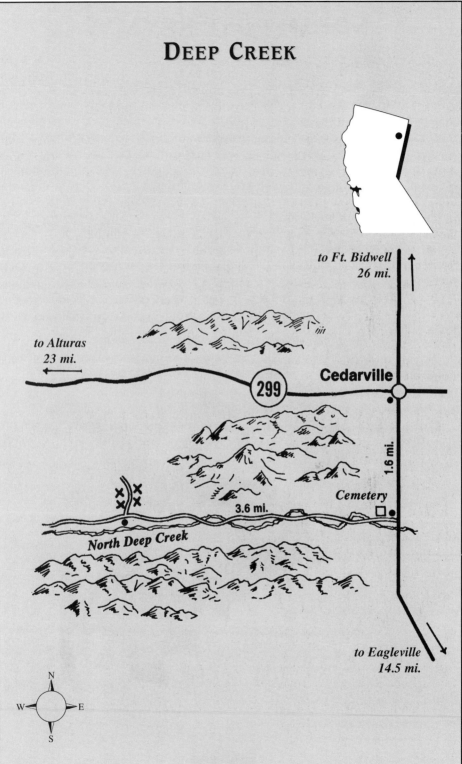

to Ft. Bidwell
26 mi.

to Alturas
23 mi.

299 **Cedarville**

1.6 mi.

Cemetery

3.6 mi.

North Deep Creek

to Eagleville
14.5 mi.

N
W E
S

NORTHWEST NEVADA

This is a long and remote trip, but the road is well graded, and there are signposts at all key turnoffs. The trip takes you through a number of vast obsidian fields. Most of the region from Site "A" through Site "D" is covered with obsidian and Apache tears. The sites shown on the map are just where the concentrations seem most intense. The road is virtually black with volcanic glass for much of the trip, making it difficult to decide exactly where to stop. If this appeals to you, take Highway 299 east from Cedarville, up the switchbacks and into Nevada. Follow the road toward Highway 140, about 46 miles, to where the ground becomes black, designating a heavy concentration of obsidian. The collecting continues for quite a distance, and all you must do is park and gather whatever you like.

Site "B" features Apache tears still embedded within the host perlite. Chunks of the porous perlite containing black tears make very nice display pieces in mineral collections, and it should be worth your time to look for specimens containing lots of little obsidianites. A hillside of this unique, grayish material will be seen on the right side of the road, at the given mileage, just past the turnoff to Badger Mountain and Summit Lake. Moonstone is also reported to have been found here, so be on the lookout.

Go another 9.7 miles to another heavy concentration of obsidian, labeled Site "C" on the map. Do as at Site "A" and roam the vast area to find the best it has to offer. Site "D" is encountered just after turning right toward Highway 140, about 2.2 miles north of Site "C". This, too, provides more obsidian and Apache tears, and the field extends about 2 miles along the road.

Some of the materials are more transparent than others, so take time to find the best. If you choose to split any specimens to determine quality and/or transparency, be sure to wear goggles and gloves.

Examining obsidian specimens in Northwest Nevada, Site B

NORTHWEST NEVADA

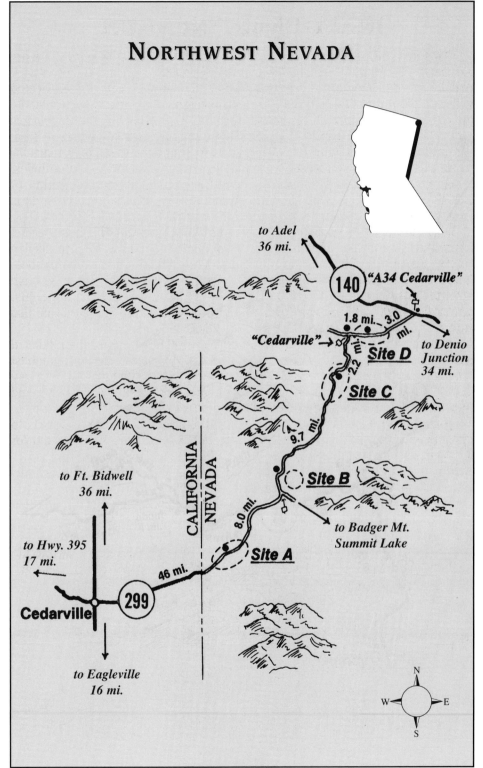

to Adel
36 mi.

140 "A34 Cedarville"

1.8 mi. 3.0 mi.

"Cedarville" Site D

to Denio
Junction
34 mi.

2.2 mi.

Site C

9.7 mi.

Site B

to Badger Mt.
Summit Lake

to Ft. Bidwell
36 mi.

CALIFORNIA

NEVADA

8.0 mi.

to Hwy. 395
17 mi.

Site A

46 mi.

299

Cedarville

to Eagleville
16 mi.

N
W E
S

GRANGER CREEK WOOD

Lots of petrified wood can be found throughout the region south of Cedarville. There are three spots in particular, which are relatively easy to get to and afford an opportunity for rockhounds to sample what this area has to offer. To get to the first, labeled Site "A" on the accompanying map, go south from town about 4 miles to Granger Creek Road, turn right and proceed another 4 miles. The wood will be found randomly scattered throughout the hills to the north, about one city block from where you must park. Simply roam the lowlands looking for the wood which may be partially buried or on the surface as chips. Pay particularly close attention to regions of erosion, since that is where you will most likely discover the more sizable pieces.

To get to Site "B", return to the highway and continue south another 4.2 miles to where you will see a gravel pit east of the road. Just a short distance farther, the road dips and crosses a large wash. That is the collecting area. Hike through the wash in either direction to gather additional petrified wood and even some nice bloodstone. The bloodstone is quite rare, but well worth looking for. It is difficult to accurately determine true quality based on a superficial examination directly from the wash, since all such pieces are dull and severely abraded, appearing to be porous and unappealing. Either split any stone you expect might be bloodstone, to better determine quality, or save all you find until back home. The best time to collect here is after a good rainstorm, since that tends to clean the rocks, making stones of interest easier to spot.

Site "C" is reached by traveling an additional 4 miles south to another wash. Fine specimen quality wood can also be found here, but it is necessary to hike a distance to the west in order to get the best the location has to offer.

Most of what can be found at these three sites tends to be of specimen quality only and rarely colorful and/or solid enough for polishing. That should not serve as a deterrent, however, since interesting pieces which accurately display the original wood structure make great conversation pieces and additions to mineral collections.

GRANGER CREEK WOOD

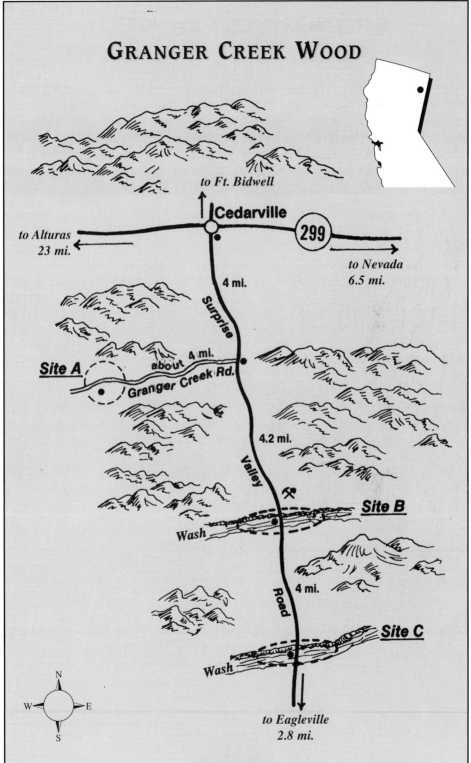

to Ft. Bidwell

Cedarville

to Alturas
23 mi.

299

to Nevada
6.5 mi.

4 mi.

Surprise

Site A

about 4 mi.

Granger Creek Rd.

4.2 mi.

Valley

Site B

Wash

Road

4 mi.

Site C

Wash

to Eagleville
2.8 mi.

N
W   E
S

PATRICK'S POINT

Many of the beaches in Northern California are noted for the agate pebbles which can be found scattered throughout their sands. Some locations, however are far more productive than others, and one of the most prolific is Agate Beach at Patrick's Point State Park, about 30 miles north of Eureka. Once inside the park, simply follow the signs to the steep, but well maintained trail, leading down to the shore. The agate pebbles are scattered randomly all over the entire beach, stretching in both directions, for quite a distance. For the most part, they are easy to spot due to their near white color which contrasts against the darker underlying sand and gravel.

Take a plastic bag so you have something to place the little stones into. No special equipment is needed, since the agate is found lying on the surface, having been washed ashore by the tides. It is best to hunt shortly after the tide has receded, since fresh material will then be exposed. If you live in the region, heavier concentrations of agate tend to occur after severe winter storms and their associated high tides. Do not venture onto the beach during such storms, but try to get there after the bad weather has subsided, and the tide is again at a low point. Another advantage of winter collecting is that fewer people will be at the beach, leaving more for the hardy few determined enough to brave the cold. If you cannot visit at that time of year, there may be fewer agates, but the nice weather and beautiful surroundings will more than make up for any mineralogical deficiency.

Be sure you pay close attention to the tides. Don't get caught in areas where you might be stranded if it comes in rapidly. The park has a few restrictions as to how much agate you can take, so be sure to ask rangers about current regulations before collecting.

PATRICK'S POINT

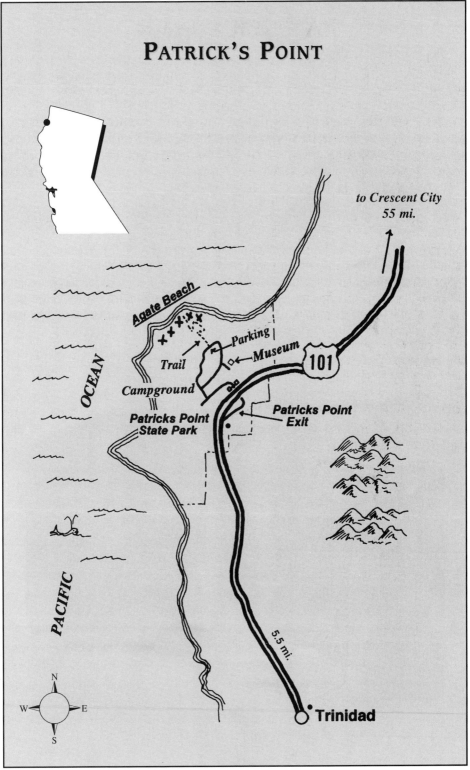

to Crescent City
55 mi.

Agate Beach

OCEAN

Parking

Trail

Museum

101

Campground

Patricks Point
State Park

Patricks Point
Exit

PACIFIC

5.5 mi.

N
W   E
S

Trinidad

WILLOW CREEK

This portion of Willow Creek boasts nice green serpentine as well as occasional specimens of agate and omphacite, a mixture of augite, jadeite and acmite. The best specimens can be cut and polished for use in most lapidary applications, including cabochons, bookends, carvings and clock faces. Obviously, the larger the specimens, the greater the likelihood for soft spots or splintering, but even those can serve as colorful display pieces in mineral collections or the harder portions can be removed for polishing.

At the given mileage along Highway 299, 5.5 miles west of Willow Creek, there is a turnout where cars can be safely parked off the pavement. From that point, it is easy to spot the trail leading down the bank to Willow Creek. Look amongst the gravel and boulders on both sides of the stream to find specimens. Be very careful if you choose to cross the river.

The serpentine is primarily green, some being very bright, and it often contains tiny black and white specks. These specks of color contrast nicely with the green and help to produce nice polished pieces. The less prevalent omphacite is generally a lighter shade of green and more granular, thereby reducing its desirability as a lapidary stone, but it can be used for colorful specimen material, and occasionally it does take a fairly good polish.

Be sure to walk a distance through the trees and brush, and don't hesitate to split any suspect stones to help in identification. If you have some time, light digging in the bank of the creek might prove fruitful.

Parked just off Highway 299 next to the Willow Creek location

WILLOW CREEK

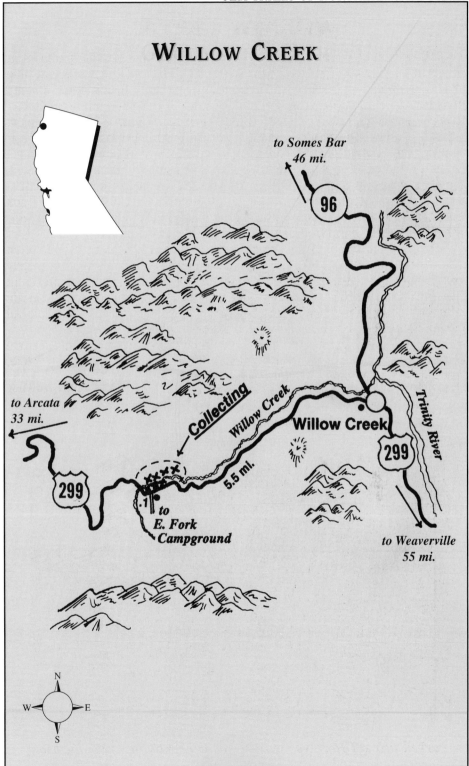

to Somes Bar
46 mi.

96

to Arcata
33 mi.

Collecting

Willow Creek

Willow Creek

Trinity River

299

5.5 ml.

299

.1
to
E. Fork
Campground

to Weaverville
55 mi.

N
W   E
S

COFFEE CREEK

Nice specimens of rhodonite, serpentine, feldspar and bornite can be found along the banks of Coffee Creek. To access this productive little waterway, head north on Highway 3 about 8 miles from Trinity Center to the Coffee Creek / Derrick Flat Road turnoff. Turn left and drive until you enter public land which is just beyond the obviously fenced-in areas. From there, and continuing at least four miles, collecting is random. Just stop where you feel lucky and inspect the rocks in and around the stream. The road somewhat parallels Coffee Creek, but does veer away from time to time. You should obviously choose to collect in regions where the road is within site of the waterway. Use good judgment if you decide to wade into Coffee Creek. Sometimes the water level is quite low and exploring the streambed, gravel bars and opposite bank is relatively safe. At other times, though, the current can be treacherous.

The rhodonite is often disguised with a black crust, so any such stones must be split in order to determine if the interior is pink. A similar situation exists with the bornite. The erosive effect of the river tarnishes exposed surfaces, making it difficult to ascertain whether or not a given stone contains bornite's telltale iridescent-like colors. Again, splitting suspect rocks to expose fresh surfaces will be necessary for best identification. The serpentine is primarily green and easy to spot, while the feldspar tends to occur in hues of pink and orange.

There is lots to be found in and around Coffee Creek, but, as is the case with just about any creek collecting, it is, for the most part, quite random in regard to where you will find the best minerals. Just be patient. There are a few mining claims along the creek and you should respect the rights of the claimholders and not collect in those areas.

COFFEE CREEK

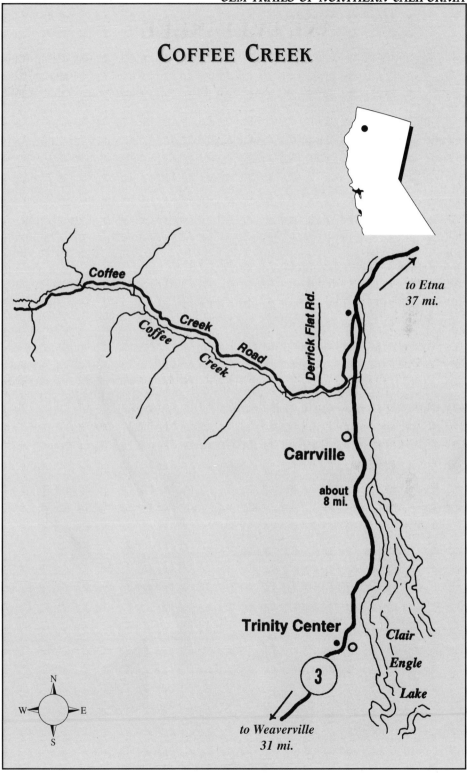

Coffee

Coffee Creek Road

Coffee Creek

Derrick Flat Rd.

to Etna
37 mi.

Carrville

about
8 mi.

Trinity Center

3

Clair
Engle
Lake

to Weaverville
31 mi.

N
W E
S

WEAVERVILLE

Serpentine, jade, jasper and agate can all be found scattered throughout the region surrounding Weaverville in just about any direction from town. The concentration is random and size somewhat limited, unless you get lucky, but the quality tends to be good. Take any of the graded dirt roads leading from Highway 3 / 299 between Weaverville and Douglas City and, when no longer on private property, park and see what can be found. If you don't find much at your first stop, drive a little farther and do it again. Pay particularly close attention to regions of erosion since fresh material is exposed and/or deposited in those areas on a fairly regular basis. If one road doesn't seem productive, try another one.

One particularly productive place to find good carving grade soapstone is in Limekiln Gulch, southeast of Weaverville. If you choose to visit Limekiln Gulch, be certain the road is dry and you have a rugged four-wheel drive vehicle, since it gets rough and steep in places. If you have doubts about you or your vehicle's ability to make such a trip, be satisfied with regions that are more accessible. If you want to give it a try, however, go south from Weaverville to where the powerline crosses the highway, about 0.7 miles from the golf course road. Continue south on Highway 3/299 another 1.3 miles and then turn left onto the graded dirt road. Continue 0.2 miles, bear right at the fork, and go another 2.6 miles to where you will again encounter the powerline. From that point, it would be wise to park and walk east along what remains of the old powerline "road". Go about 0.1 miles to where Limekiln Gulch intersects from the south, as illustrated on the map. Light green and gray soapstone can be found in the rubble throughout much of the gulch and one of the primary deposits will be seen higher up, a few tenths of a mile south of the powerline.

Be reminded again that this is a rough and potentially hazardous journey. Most collectors should be satisfied just exploring the more accessible regions. It is a scenic and restful place to visit and the minerals you find will only add to the pleasure.

WEAVERVILLE

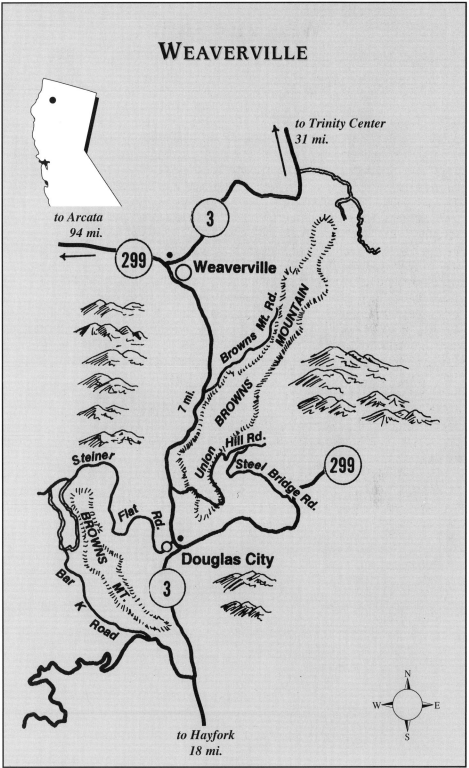

DOUGLAS CITY

This site provides collectors with an opportunity to gather nice specimens of ancient fossilized clam shells – on a hillside in the middle of the forest. To get to the fascinating little deposit, start in Douglas City and head south on Highway 3. From where Highway 3 intersects Highway 299, go 3.1 miles, as illustrated on the map, turn left (south), go another 1.6 miles to Blanchard Flat, then turn left again, driving another 1.2 miles to the old Blanchard School. The fossilized clam deposit is situated in the cliffs directly behind the school, and the main digging area can be seen from down below. It is hard to imagine this area was once part of a large sea, but the clams serve as indisputable evidence that this region was in fact, at one time, under water.

There is a dim trail leading up to the primary fossil bearing regions which comprise the main collecting area. Depending upon how much recent activity there has been here, the trail may be somewhat overgrown but that should only present a small hindrance. Once at the fossil bearing strata, it is not difficult to remove chunks of rock containing the well-preserved fossilized shells with a small sledge hammer and chisel. If you don't feel like engaging in such work, specimens can also be found by going through the rubble down below. This site is on private land, but, in the past, there have been no restrictions related to collecting, as long as no damage is done to the landscape. It would probably be a good idea to confirm current collecting status either from someone in Blanchard Flat or at the school, if anyone can be found.

DOUGLAS CITY

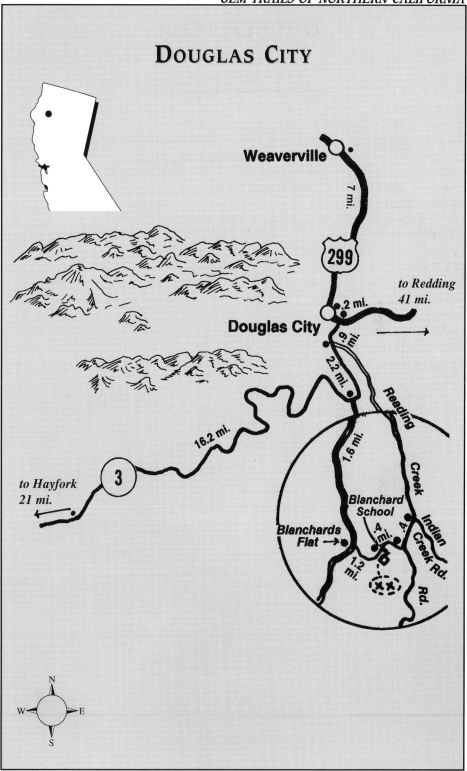

Weaverville

7 mi.

299

to Redding
41 mi.

.2 mi.

Douglas City

.9 mi.

2.2 mi.

Reading

1.6 mi.

16.2 mi.

to Hayfork
21 mi.

3

Blanchard
School

Blanchards
Flat

.4
mi.

.4

Indian
Creek Rd.

Creek

Rd.

1.2
mi.

N
W E
S

HAYFORK

This location affords rockhounds willing to commit themselves to a challenging hike through a somewhat remote area lots of good quality travertine onyx. Be advised, however, that the trip should only be taken by the most ambitious and physically fit collectors. To get there from Douglas City, drive southwest 19.5 miles along Highway 3 to the Wildwood turnoff, as shown on the map. Go south 1.5 miles toward Wildwood, at that point, the East Fork Divide Trail intersects, and the trailhead is on the east side of the road. Pull well off the pavement and prepare yourself for a challenging trek through a picturesque and pristine region.

DO NOT, under any circumstances, attempt the trip if you are not physically capable. This is a remote location, and getting help in the event of an emergency would be difficult. You will need a rock pick, goggles, gloves and a chisel or two, as well as a sturdy bag or backpack in which to carry everything. Remember that your tools must be packed in and out, and any mineral specimens you decide to keep must be carried all the way back to your vehicle. Take plenty to drink, wear good shoes, do not even think about making the hike in bad or threatening weather, and leave early in the day since you do not want to be returning in the dark unless you are equipped to spend the night.

Proceed up and along the trail approximately 4 miles. For most average hikers, the walk will take about two and one-half hours, **one way**, and you should modify that estimate to suit your own hiking pace. When walking, it is very tough to estimate when you have gone the required mileage, since one mile often feels like two or three miles. When you do reach the collecting spot, the whitish travertine deposit will easily be seen, primarily north of the trail. So, when you feel you are closing in, keep a sharp lookout for the deposit.

HAYFORK

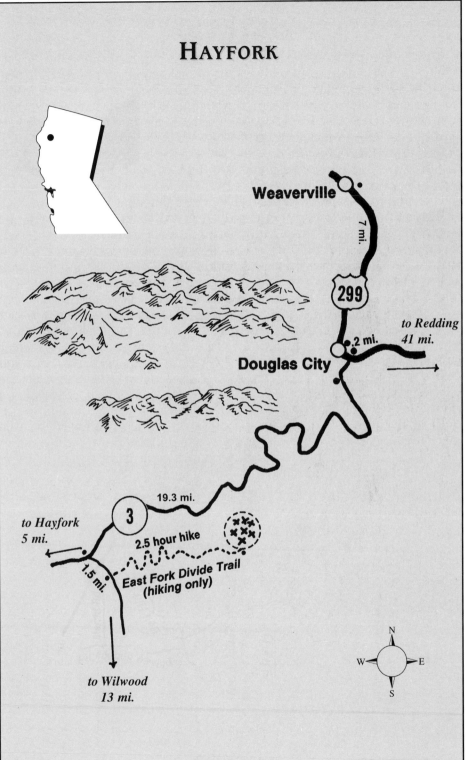

Weaverville

7 mi.

299

to Redding
41 mi.

.2 mi.

Douglas City

19.3 mi.

3

to Hayfork
5 mi.

2.5 hour hike

1.5 mi.

East Fork Divide Trail
(hiking only)

to Wilwood
13 mi.

N
W · E
S

BIG FLAT

The Big Flat Recreation Area is just about the only spot within the Shasta-Trinity National Forest open to the public for gold panning. To get there, take Highway 299 approximately 20 miles west from Weaverville to where the campground access is encountered alongside the historically dependable gold bearing Trinity River. Go right at the Forest Service sign designating Wheel Gulch Road, and proceed about 100 yards to the campground entrance. Access to the Trinity River is on the opposite side of Highway 299, but only a few hundred yards from the campground. Be careful when crossing the pavement.

No fee is charged for recreational gold panning within the designated campground limits, since it is all on government land, but if you have a small dredge and want to use it, you must first get a permit from the California Department of Fish and Game, License and Revenue Branch, 3211 S. Street, Sacramento CA 95816, (916) 227-2245. The cost of the permit is $37.50 for California residents and $147.25 for nonresidents. Specific local information to assist with your gold searching efforts can be obtained at the Big Bar Ranger Station about three miles farther west. Most visitors to this location are satisfied with simple gold panning and occasionally their patience does pay off with nice flakes and tiny nuggets. The campground has ten units, potable water, and toilets. Trailers under 22 feet in length are permitted. The campground is open all year – even though it can get quite cold in the winter - and the fee to stay, at time of publication, was $8.00 per day. If the campground is full when you visit, additional camping is available at nearby Big Bar and Pigeon Point. Supplies can be picked up in the nearby town of Big Bar.

If you want advance information about weather and/or accessibility to the campground, contact the Big Bar Ranger Station (530) 623-6106. If you want information in regard to gold panning techniques, it is suggested that you obtain a good book on the subject before leaving home.

BIG FLAT

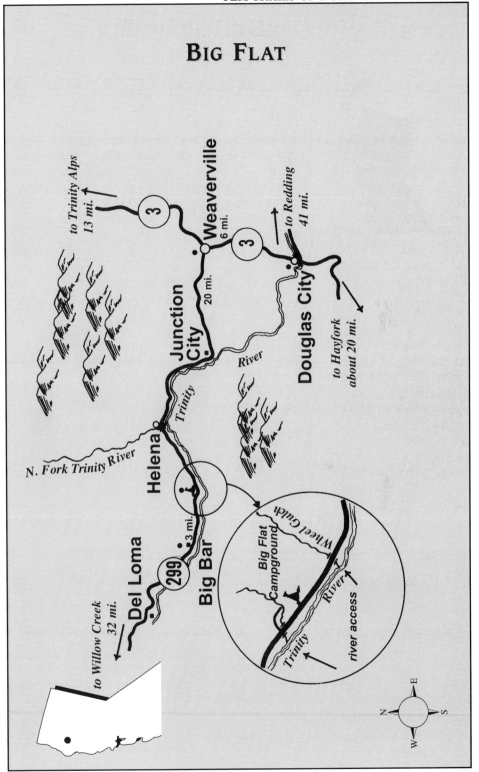

VAN DUZEN RIVER

Fine specimens of green and red jasper can be found throughout the river gravels and boulders strewn alongside the Van Duzen River, near Grizzly Creek State Park. In addition, serpentine and, rarely, some jade, can also be obtained. There is no particular spot to stop. Just look for an easily accessible portion of the river, or any of its tributaries, and search. The Van Duzen River is often quite treacherous, so do not be tempted to try wading across to see what can be found on the opposite banks. Either cross at locations where a road does so, or be satisfied with what can be obtained on the highway side.

Remember that river rocks are often very abraded and dull on the surface. Therefore, any suspect stone should be split open to expose a fresh surface to more accurately reveal its true desirability. So many beautifully colored specimens are tossed away because the surface looks so unappealing.

Do not park your vehicle on the road when you do decide to stop. There are many adequate places to pull off along this stretch of Highway 36, so keep an eye out for them. Be advised that Grizzly Creek State Park offers a scenic place to stop, but no collecting is allowed there. Hiking upstream, outside the Park's boundary, however, may provide additional collectibles. Just be certain you are out of the Park before picking anything up.

This is a great location to spend a few days, especially during the summer months. The best time to search is when the rivers is low, thereby exposing more of the mineral bearing banks and gravel bars.

VAN DUZEN RIVER

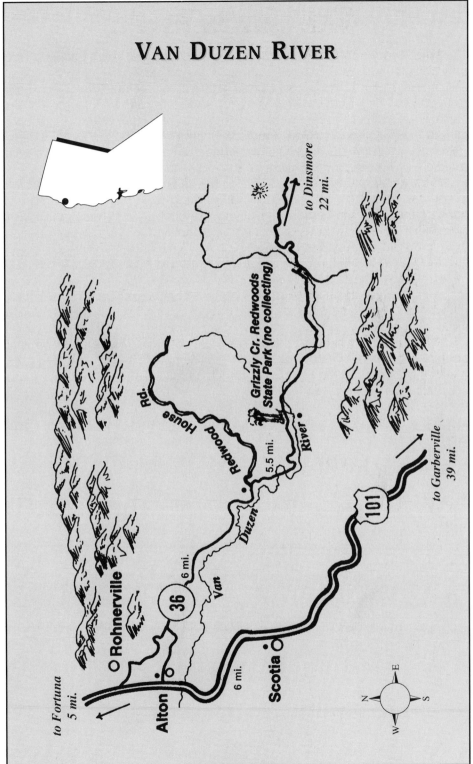

to Dinsmore
22 mi.

Grizzly Cr. Redwoods
State Park (no collecting)

5.5 mi.

Redwood House Rd.

River

101

to Garberville
39 mi.

Van Duzen

6 mi.

Rohnerville

36

6 mi.

Scotia

6 mi.

Alton

to Fortuna
5 mi.

N
E
S
W

RUTH

Areas surrounding the Mad River, especially near the small town of Ruth, offer rockhounds lots of jasper and agate, as well as occasional manganese specimens. To get to the most accessible stretch of the Mad River, go south from Hayfork on Highway 3 to where it intersects Highway 36, head west about 20 miles more to the small town of Mad River, and, finally, turn south along Lower Mad River Road. From that point, all along the river's banks, there is good potential for finding something of interest. Just stop, from time to time, as you head for Ruth, about 16 miles away.

The best concentrations seem to be in the immediate vicinity of Ruth, both along the banks of the Mad River as well as throughout the terrain surrounding the town. Just be certain you do not trespass onto private property. If something looks especially promising on private land, either seek permission to trespass or do not collect there.

The Mad River can be a powerful waterway, and you should not consider trying to wade into it unless the water level is low enough to be safe. There is a crossing at the dam on the north end of Ruth Reservoir if you want to inspect the western side, and that is about the only consistently convenient and safe place to get across.

This is a location where it takes some patient searching. If you find little or nothing at one particular stop, simply head on a little farther and try again. Also remember that river worn rocks are often abraded and dull, thereby making their colors appear very pale, when, in reality, that might not actually be the case. If you spot any stones with color, even if a light hue, be sure to look at them more closely or split them to expose a fresh surface. Pale, water worn, yellow, orange or white exteriors may conceal beautiful rich color inside.

RUTH

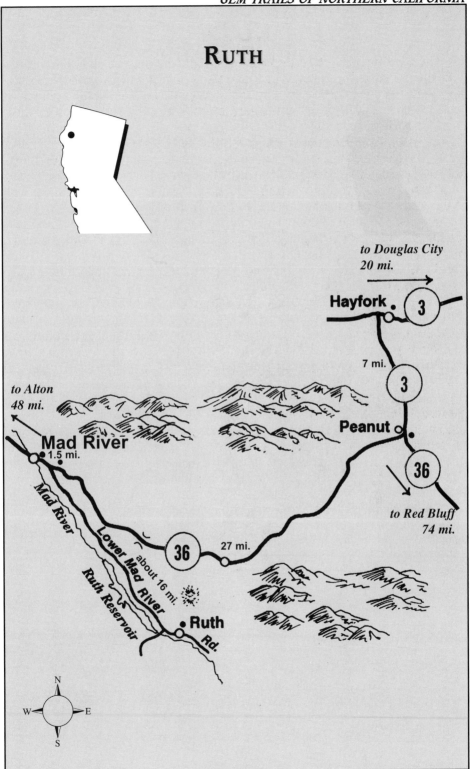

to Douglas City
20 mi.

Hayfork ③

7 mi.

③

to Alton
48 mi.

Peanut

Mad River

1.5 mi.

Mad River

Lower Mad River

36

to Red Bluff
74 mi.

36   27 mi.

about 16 mi.

Ruth Reservoir

Ruth Rd.

N
W   E
S

BUTTE CREEK

The Butte Creek Recreation Area offers rockhounds 23 gold mining and mineral collecting sites upon which to pursue their hobby. A prospecting permit is not needed for day-use and/or low-impact gold panning, but it is required if you want to use a dredge. To get a permit, contact the California Department of Fish and Game, License and Revenue Branch, 3211 S Street, Sacramento CA 95816, (916) 227-2245. Be advised, in spite of the fact that the camping area is open all year, dredging is only allowed from the fourth Saturday in May until October 15th. Most visitors, however, are only interested in simple panning and walking around looking for mineral specimens.

The site is administered by the Redding BLM office at 355 Hemsted Drive, Redding, CA 96002, (530) 224-2100 and it offers a most beautiful and productive place to spend some time. The primitive campground provides nice flat places upon which to set up a tent, and easy access to gold-bearing Butte Creek. If you want to camp and do some recreational rockhounding or panning, the usage fee, at time of publication, is $5.00 per day.

To get there, proceed northeast 16 miles along Highway 32 from Chico to the small town of Forest Ranch. In Forest Ranch, the BLM suggests heading southeast on Doe Mill Road 3.5 miles to the Butte Creek trailhead, but, unless that road is new, the traditional route is to continue another 3.3 miles along Highway 32 to Garland Road and then double back 3.2 miles to where it intersects Doe Mill Road. From there, go left another 2.3 miles to the bridge leading over the river to the camping area.

There are some nice hiking trails along the river between Forks of Butte and the De Sabla Powerhouse, and, along the way, you will see an occasional mine dump which affords potential for finding metallic ores such as pyrite and galena. Be aware that there is lots of restricted land in this region, so only collect and/or pan in permissible places. For more information on collecting regulations be sure to contact the Redding BLM office before your departure.

It is also advisable to take warm clothes with you since, even in the summer, the temperatures can get quite cool. If you need some instruction in regard to gold panning it is recommended that you obtain a good book on the subject before leaving home.

BUTTE CREEK

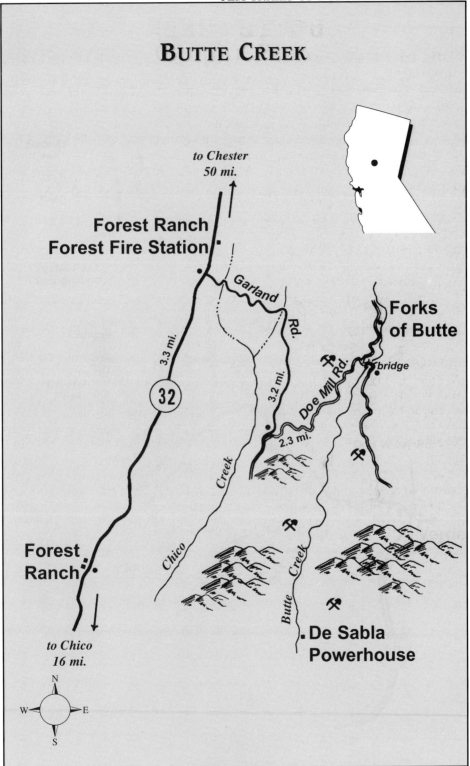

to Chester
50 mi.

Forest Ranch
Forest Fire Station

Garland Rd.

Forks
of Butte

3.3 mi.

32

3.2 mi.

Doe Mill Rd.

bridge

2.3 mi.

Creek

Chico

Forest
Ranch

Butte Creek

to Chico
16 mi.

De Sabla
Powerhouse

N
W   E
S

BELDEN

If you would like to try your luck at gold prospecting, the North Fork of the Feather River, near the small town of Belden, provides great opportunities. Be advised, however, that most river access in this region is protected by mining claims, so special permission is needed to pan in any such area. One way to get that permission and, in the process, also receive free placer mining instruction is through the Golden Caribou Mining Club, with seasonal headquarters at the Caribou Corner Cafe and Caribou Crossroads Campground. This is not a site for everybody, but the lessons and a chance to prospect on consistently productive areas may be of interest to some readers.

If you want to go, the Caribou Corner Cafe and Campground is located on Caribou Road, just off Highway 70, about 27 miles west of Quincy. It is important that you make advance arrangements before heading there by contacting the Golden Caribou Mining Club directly at P.O. Box 300, Belden, CA 95915. You can also e-mail them to make specific arrangements or clarify questions at either GCMC2002@aol.com or GCMC4ME@aol.com. and, finally, the club website is: http://www.golden-caribou.com. The campground phone number is (530) 283-1384. The free gold panning and sluice box operation lessons are offered just about any day from June through September for first-time gold panners. If you would like a more thorough tour of the club's claims, free of charge, they are conducted on the 3rd weekend of each month.

This is not an endorsement for this particular mining club, but the free instruction and relative consistency of gold production comes with high recommendations. In addition, the club supplies all the equipment, shows you how to use it, and, if desired, offers an opportunity to join them, thereby gaining access to all their approximately 1,500 acres of gold claims.

BELDEN

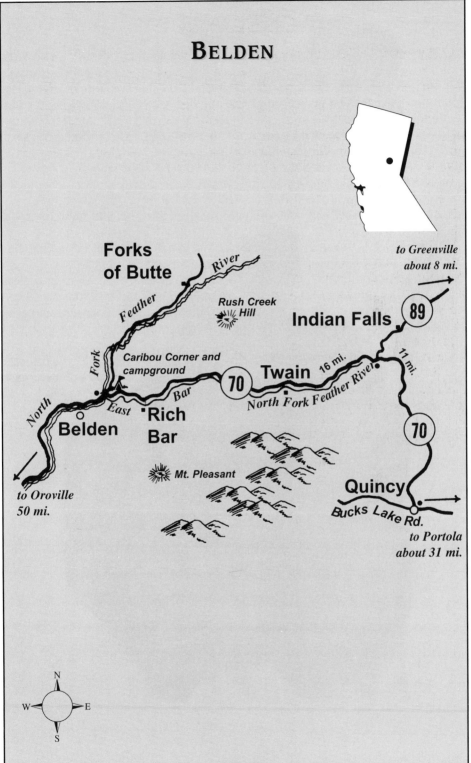

JACKS VALLEY

This collecting site offers rockhounds an opportunity to find a good variety of colorful jasper, agate and petrified wood. To get there, start in Susanville and follow Highway 139 north from town 10.5 miles to the Jacks Valley Monument. At that point, go west onto the dirt road. From the moment you leave the pavement, continuing at least 1.5 miles, there is agate, jasper, and petrified wood randomly scattered in all directions. Pay particularly close attention to the areas of erosion, especially along the banks of the creek to the south. Be careful if you scramble into the lower valley since the terrain is unstable and it would be easy to slip. As you head down, keep an eye out for minerals of interest. Frequently there will be pieces of petrified wood protruding from the relatively soft soil, and some of the colorful jasper might be spotted along the way.

When in regions near the riverbed be reminded that anything that has been carried any distance by the waterway might be very abraded on the surface and cause otherwise brilliantly colored jasper and good clean and clear agate to look uninteresting. Any stone that seems as though it may have had its surface "tumbled" should be sprayed with water and/or split to show its true desirability.

Most of the wood is brown and the jasper come in shades of orange, brown and red, with most being somewhat small. The agate is clear or gray with black inclusions. Concentrations vary greatly, so, if you don't find much at one spot, simply move a little farther along and try again.

The road leading through Jacks Valley site

JACKS VALLEY

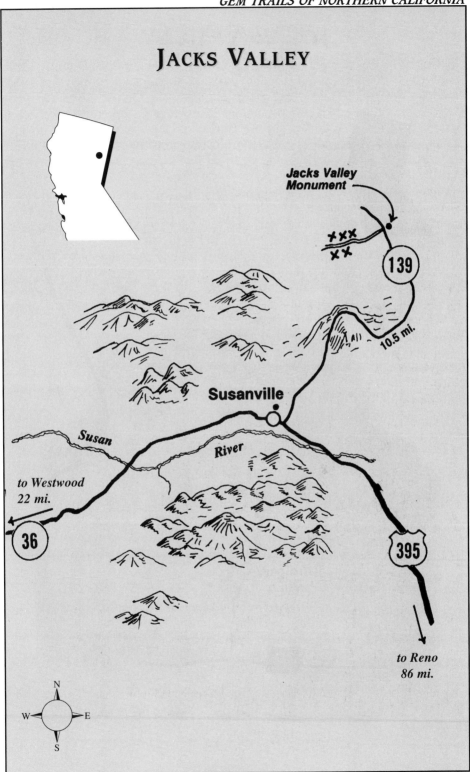

Jacks Valley
Monument

139

10.5 mi.

Susanville

Susan   River

to Westwood
22 mi.

36

395

to Reno
86 mi.

N
W   E
S

SUSANVILLE

Colorful jasper, agate, petrified wood, serpentine and Apache tears are the minerals of interest in the region illustrated on the accompanying map. To get there from Susanville, go east along Highway 36 for 6.1 miles to where Highway 44 intersects. Continue another 3.6 miles to the graded dirt Forest Service road leading south from the pavement. This road parallels the west side of Willard Creek and should not be confused with Willard Creek Road, a short distance farther east, which goes entirely through private property and is off limits to collectors.

Simply park just about anywhere along the Forest Service road, and walk eastward to the stream. This location provides some nice clear, gray and white agate, frequently filled with interesting black inclusions. There is also some red and green agate which makes beautiful polished pieces if you are lucky enough to find some. The wood tends to be tan or ash-white and the jasper comes in shades of orange, brown, yellow and red, some interlaced with black inclusions. Most of what can be found here is relatively small, but generally of good quality capable of taking a nice polish. There are occasional chunks of green serpentine, and even some little Apache tears scattered randomly throughout the area.

Be advised that much of the material is difficult to spot, since it has been rounded and abraded by the river. Be sure to carefully scrutinize any suspect stone you might encounter. Explore the creek bed, both banks, and the flatlands stretching for quite a distance in all directions. The site offers great variety and quality, but nothing is overly plentiful.

Collecting at Susanville

SUSANVILLE

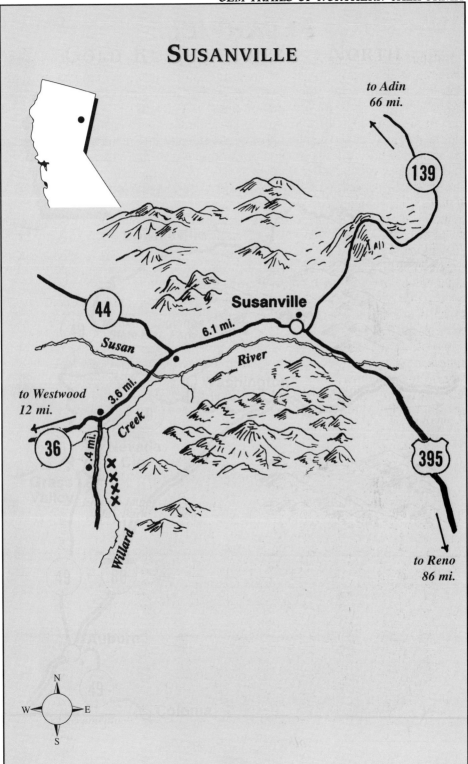

to Adin
66 mi.

139

44

Susanville

6.1 mi.

Susan

River

to Westwood
12 mi.

3.6 mi.

36

Creek

.4 mi.

×××××

Willard

395

to Reno
86 mi.

N
W   E
S

ALDERPOINT

This collecting site is very easy to find due to the large amount of green serpentine scattered all over the road and surrounding terrain. Not only can rockhounds gather the nice carving grade serpentine here, but colorful jasper and chert can also be picked up with very little effort.

To get to this productive locality, go 2.1 miles northeast from Alderpoint on the road to Zenia, as shown on the accompanying map. There, you should go right, toward Kettenpom, on Hoagland Peak Road. Continue on that well-graded gravel road about 7.8 miles to where, on the north, a huge boulder of bright green serpentine can be seen. That marks the center of this rather extensive collecting area.

Material can be found scattered throughout the terrain for quite a distance in all directions. The serpentine is green and white, often containing tiny black inclusions. Some is quite grainy, fibrous, and/or flaky though, so take time to find only the best. Chunks displaying both green and white are more prized than solid shades of green, and pieces containing lots of the tiny black specks are even more desirable for use in producing interesting polished pieces.

The Jasper and chert primarily occur in shades of brown, the most highly prized being a deep chocolate hue, but bright orange specimens also can be found scattered about. There is also a most unusual variety of jasper composed of contrasting white and black streaks which polishes nicely.

Do not hesitate to do some walking, since it seems that the finest material is usually a distance from the road, partially hidden by shrubbery. Take a rock pick with you to use for splitting any suspect stones in an effort to ascertain their true identity and quality.

Collecting at Alderpoint

ALDERPOINT

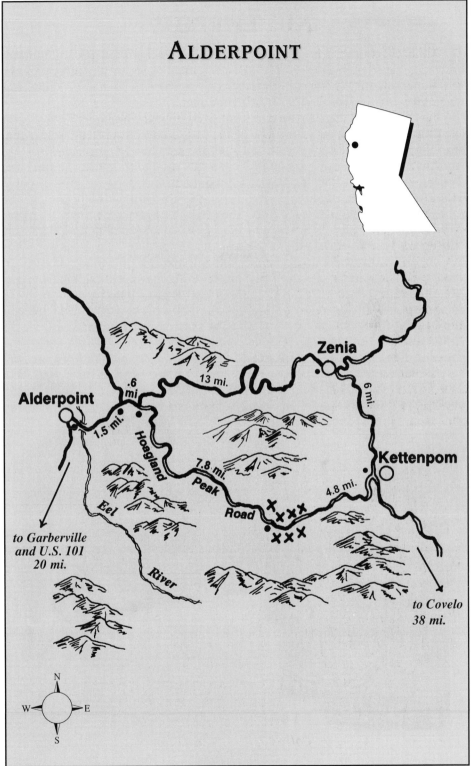

Zenia

13 mi.

6 mi.

.6 mi

Alderpoint

1.5 mi.

Hoagland

7.8 mi.

Peak

Kettenpom

4.8 mi.

Road

Eel

*to Garberville
and U.S. 101
20 mi.*

River

*to Covelo
38 mi.*

N
W   E
S

KETTENPOM

Serpentine, jasper, chert, and even a few chunks of jade can be found on both sides of the road, not only at the general location illustrated on the accompanying map, but at numerous additional places all along the route connecting Covelo and the tiny town of Kettenpom.

The site shown on the map extends throughout the brush and trees for at least one-half mile in all directions. Pay close attention to areas of erosion, especially the ditch on the east side. The quality varies considerably, but worthwhile quantities of gem material can be found with minimal effort. The serpentine is green, and it occasionally contains nice, bright white regions. Most, however, tend to be flaky and unsuitable for cutting and polishing, but some are hard enough. Lots of the serpentine possesses such a nice shade of green that many collectors simply clean it up and display it in their mineral collections, as is, with no polishing.

The chert and jasper are brownish-red and maroon, and generally occur in smaller sizes. As with the serpentine, much of it tends to be unsuitable for polishing, due to its porous nature. There is lots of good hard material here, so be sure to carefully examine all that you find. The colors are not brilliant, but more subtle. That can be very desirable for some lapidary applications.

Excellent specimens of all the minerals can be found if you have the patience. It might be necessary to use a shovel for removing large, partially buried boulders, and a grass rake may be handy for clearing pine needles in an effort to expose underlying stones. Most material is found on the surface, though, and such heavy labor probably is unnecessary. *DO NOT*, under any circumstances, dig into the road!

Searching for specimens along the side of the road

KETTENPOM

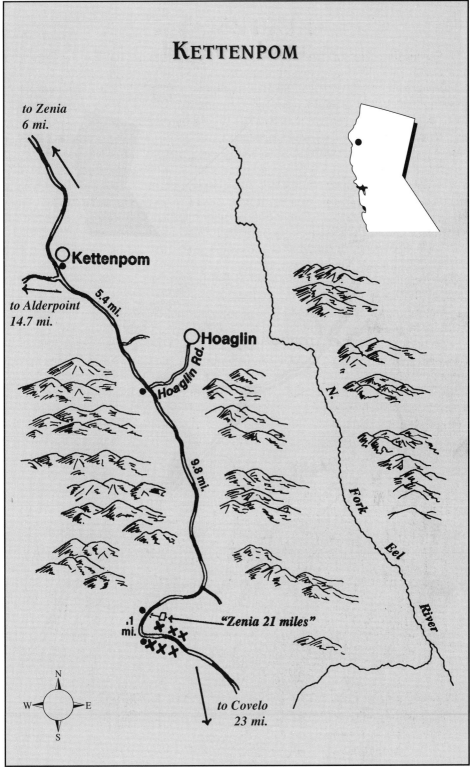

to Zenia
6 mi.

Kettenpom

5.4 mi.

to Alderpoint
14.7 mi.

Hoaglin Rd.   Hoaglin

9.8 mi.

N. Fork Eel River

.1
mi.

✕✕✕
✕✕✕

"Zenia 21 miles"

to Covelo
23 mi.

N
W   E
S

COVELO

Fine specimens of green serpentine, jade and jasper can be found at this scenic locality. The collecting is done primarily along the Eel River, just west of the bridge, as illustrated on the map. Even though each of the minerals found here is worthwhile, the jade, obviously, is the most prized. As you would expect, though, it is also the most difficult to find.

The best jasper is brightly colored, in shades of red, rust, gold, and brown, some have fine white stringers. It is very easy to spot, since the native rock is a neutral gray. The brilliant hues of the jasper seem to stand out like little colored lights against the nondescript gravel and rock. Just start walking through the area to spot it. Jasper isn't overly plentiful however, and even though quality tends to be quite good, some are porous and dull. Take enough time to procure the best. Your patience should be well rewarded!

Jade and serpentine range in color from dark green to white, most of which is mottled, and the quality varies greatly. Some are flaky and/or poorly colored, so be sure to take enough time to find the best. More can be picked up along nearby Williams Creek, a short distance west, but the best collecting there is done on private property. Inquire in Covelo or at the Black Butte Store if you want more information. Do not trespass without getting permission in advance. If you cannot contact the landowners, restrict your search to open regions.

This site is quite extensive, and you should be able to find nice specimens for quite a distance along the river. If you choose to cross the river, do so over the bridge near the Ranger station. There are deep pools hidden throughout the riverbed, and the current can be intense. If the water level is high, do not even attempt wading. If it appears safe, good specimens can sometimes be found on the

gravel bars as well as on the banks. That is especially true after a severe storm, when fresh material may be washed downstream. Again, do not enter the river if there is any doubt as to the safety.

Looking for minerals alongside the Eel River, below the Covelo site bridge

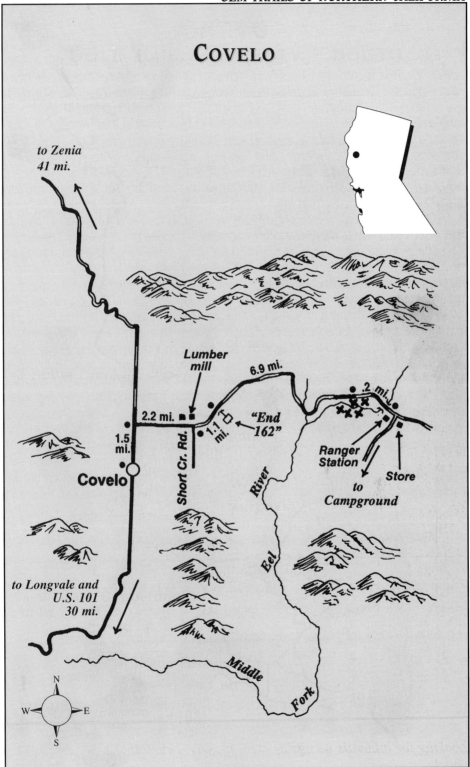

COVELO

to Zenia
41 mi.

Lumber
mill

6.9 mi.

2 mi.

2.2 mi.

1.1
mi.

"End
162"

1.5
mi.

Short Cr. Rd.

River

Ranger
Station

Store

Covelo

Eel

to
Campground

to Longvale and
U.S. 101
30 mi.

Middle

Fork

N
W   E
S

MINA

The two sites illustrated on the accompanying map are situated in a most scenic locality. However, this is not a winter trip, since the weather can become severe at that time of year. Save this expedition for the summer, late spring or early fall. Keep in mind, as you take this drive, that the two specific spots discussed here are, by no means, the only places that might be of interest to rockhounds along this stretch of road. If you have the time, try to stop and inspect roadside rocks as often as possible. The entire region is well known for its fine serpentine, jade, jasper, and other cutting materials. Outstanding specimens have been picked up randomly throughout the hills, streams, and roads between Covelo and Kettenpom.

Site "A" is situated along the Eel River, and it extends for quite a distance in either direction from the bridge, about 17 miles north of Covelo. Park well off the road and *carefully* hike down to the river. The climb down is **not easy**, and care should be taken, since it can be quite hazardous. If you do not feel capable of the climb, **do not do it!**

When at the river, search through the gravel and boulders, on either side, for jade, serpentine, and crocidolite. The crocidolite is a blue, fibrous variety of riebeckite, and larger specimens make excellent display pieces. The jade and serpentine occur in shades of green and white, and the quality varies considerably. Sizes vary from tiny pebbles to large boulders. Take time to walk a distance along the river to find the best specimens, but do not attempt crossing, since the currents can be treacherous. If you want to search the opposite bank, climb back out, cross the bridge, and descend again.

Site "B" is near where the tiny community of Mina once stood. Nothing of the town is left, but it is located 2.8 miles north of the Eel River bridge. Look beside the road and throughout the trees and shrubs for chunks of maroon and purple chert, most of which will take a dull polish. Some of the material is quite colorful and can be used to make nice cabochons.

North Fork of the Eel River at the Mina locality

MINA

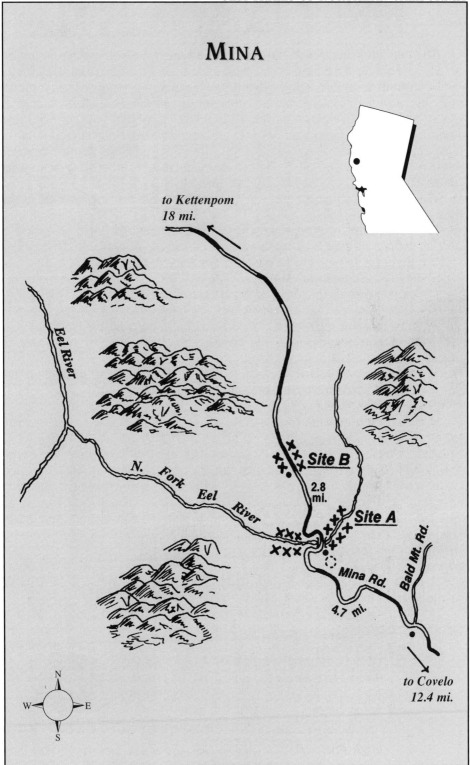

to Kettenpom
18 mi.

Eel River

N. Fork Eel River

Site B
2.8 mi.

Site A

Mina Rd.

Bald Mt. Rd.

4.7 mi.

to Covelo
12.4 mi.

N
W   E
S

TUMBLE POLISHING ROCKS

Much of the material that can be found while rock collecting can be tumble polished. Tumbling is the form of stone polishing through which a large segment of rockhounds get in to as a gem hobby. It is a relatively easy craft which produces really beautiful gemstones that can be used in an almost endless variety of jewelry and decorator items. Once the "bug" has bitten you, you may well find yourself branching out into other types of gem cutting and jewelry making. Whatever route you follow, you can be assured you are going to spend many enjoyable, relaxing hours, and you will be able to turn out creations of striking beauty for personal use, gifts, and/or a profitable part-time business.

The following equipment and supplies are needed to become involved in the craft of gemstone tumbling:

(1) **Equipment.** Appropriately, the machine that is used is called a *tumbler*. There is a wide variety of tumblers available, and prices range from quite low to medium, for the most part.

(2) **Rough Gemstone Material.** Many various types of stones are tumble polished, some of the better-known being petrified wood, agate and jade. Craftsmen in this field collect much of the material they use in the deserts, mountains, and in many other locations. The other major source for stones, especially those not available in local areas, is a rock shop or catalog supplier. There you will find rough and polished gemstones; supplies and tools; equipment for all kinds of gem cutting; and mineral and crystal specimens.

(3) **Abrasive (Grit).** *Silicon carbide*, a man-made abrasive in a loose grain or powder form that is used for grinding and smoothing the stones in a tumbler.

(4) **A Polishing Agent.** The final finish is most often accomplished with a polishing powder, usually an oxide of some metal. *Grit* and polishing agents are also sold by rock shops and catalog suppliers.

All of these items may be purchased separately, or some manufacturers do combine them in kit form. In addition to the equipment and materials listed above, these kits usually include a supply of jewelry parts, a tube of jewelry cement and an instruction book. It's a convenient and inexpensive means for getting started in the craft.

There is a wide variety of gem materials available, many of which looks beautiful when tumble polished. They come from three sources:

(1) **Natural minerals formed in the earth.** A few examples of this category include agate, turquoise, garnet, petrified wood and malachite.

(2) **Products of animal or plant life**, such as pearls, coral or amber.

(3) **Man-made materials.** These include synthetics, which are laboratory duplicates of nature, such as synthetic rubies and sapphires.

Of the three categories above, the people who tumble gems use mostly material from the first, the natural stones.

Gold Rush Country Quartz Crystals

Hanging Rock Canyon Sulfur

Malachite from the Mount Shasta collecting site

Patrick's Point Unpolished Beach Agate

Jade found at Jade Cove

Moss Agate

Etna Marble

Petrified Wood From Granger Creek

Davis Creek Obsidian and Obsidian Needles

Pyrite from Gold Valley

Hayden Hill Rhyolite and Jasper

Bear River Area Feldspar, Mica and Quartz Crystal

Kelseyville Jasper and Obsidian

Coffee Creek Bornite

Mazourka Canyon Fossil Coral

Pyrite in Quartz, Bridge port

Big Pine Smoky Quart Crystals

Agate Beach "Oil Agate"

Mina Jade and Serpentine

Petrified Wood

Jade and Rhodonite from Happy Camp

Fossil Twigs

Selection of Agates and Jaspers

Carnelian from Jenny Creek

TUMBLE POLISHING ROCKS (CONT'D)

There are many other ways of classifying gemstones. One is the amount of light that can penetrate the material. Thus we have: transparent, semi-transparent, translucent and opaque. All are used for tumble polished gems, but you will probably see more opaque and translucent.

Another classification is by hardness, which in the mineral field is thought of as the ability of one stone to scratch another. This is quite important to the rockhound because generally (not always), the harder the gemstones, the more time required to work it, and the higher polish it will take. Also, the harder the stone, the longer it should retain its polish for there will be fewer substances in its environment that can scratch it.

Friedrich Mohs (1773-1839), a mineralogist, devised a scale for showing hardness with numerical designations of 1 for the softest through 10 for the hardest.

The Mohs Scale of Hardness

1 –	Talc	6 –	Feldspar
2 –	Gypsum	7 –	Quartz
3 –	Calcite	8 –	Topaz
4 –	Fluorite	9 –	Corundum
5 –	Apatite	10 –	Diamond

It should be stated that these are relative hardnesses only. The Mohs Scale simply states that the stones listed will scratch any of those with lower numbers.

It is generally recommended that no material softer than glass be tumbled because they can be scratched easily, ruining the polish. In fact, it is a good idea not to use anything softer than quartz for items that can receive rough treatment—on a key chain, for instance. It is better to use softer stones for earrings, pendants, etc. Exceptions to this rule are the two types of jade, jadeite and nephrite. Although softer than quartz, they do not scratch easily.

For people who collect their own materials in the field, quite a few rock shops and catalog suppliers sell hardness testing kits. These consist of various minerals listed on the Mohs Scale. Inexpensive kits simply have samples of the minerals. On the better sets, pieces of the minerals are mounted in pencil-like handles for easier use.

Tumble polishing is man's improvement on a process that nature has been carrying out for ages. Tons of gemstones are tumbled commercially and sold at reasonable prices. But if you are a do-it-yourselfer, you can save money and have fun tumble polishing your own gems.

From *How to Tumble Polish Gemstones and Make Tumbled Jewelry* by Jerome Wexler.

HEARST

Jade, banded rhyolite, actinolite, and jasper can all be found along the Eel River, about 13 miles northeast of Willits, near the townsite of Hearst. To reach this collecting location, follow the directions illustrated on the accompanying map. The road is not bad, even after the pavement ends, and most passenger cars should be able to make the trip, if driven carefully.

As you approach the given mileage, be on the lookout for a bridge on the left, crossing the river. That marks the center of the site. There are plenty of places to park off the road, and all you must do is walk to the edge of the river and start your search.

Hike any direction along the river, looking for minerals. The jade, serpentine and actinolite primarily occur in shades of green. The jasper is red, yellow, orange, and white, in a variety of combinations and patterns, and the rhyolite can be found in hues of rust, orange and brown. Due to the colorful nature of all these minerals, they tend to be fairly easy to spot against the more neutral native rocks and gravel.

The mineral of prime interest is jade, and while the finest hue is green, much of it contains areas of white, and collectors have also reported finding some prize blue jade here. Much of it is solid enough for use in carvings and cabochons, but a lot is either highly fractured, lacking good color, or splintery. Take plenty of time to adequately search both sides of the river, as far as you can, for the best the site has to offer. Do not, however, wade too far, since there are often stiff currents and deep potholes. Walk over the bridge to gain access to the opposite side.

The jasper can be found alongside the river as well as on the adjacent flatlands. Some is grainy and incapable of taking a good polish, but there is lots of top quality material. As with the jade, you must have patience and be willing to do some exploration to locate the best.

Bridge crossing the Eel River, at center of Hearst collecting site

HEARST

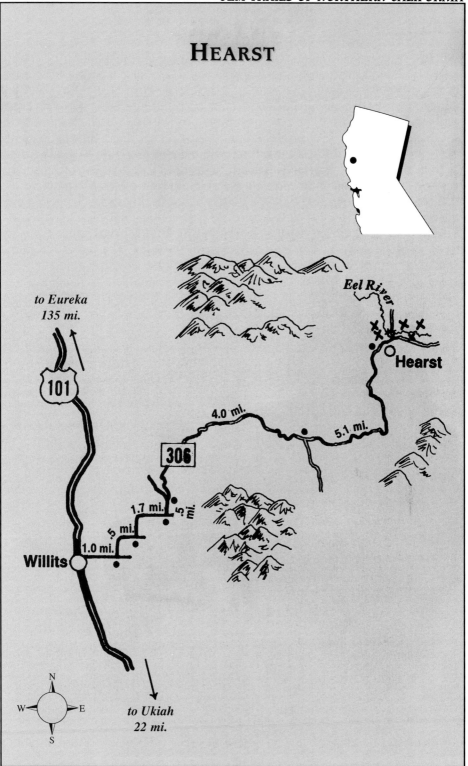

to Eureka
135 mi.

101

Eel River

✕ ✕ ✕

Hearst

4.0 mi.

306

5.1 mi.

1.7 mi.

.5 mi.

.5 mi.

.5 mi.

Willits

1.0 mi.

N
W — E
S

to Ukiah
22 mi.

STONY CREEK

The region surrounding the Black Butte Reservoir is noted for its colorful jasper and occasional chunks of petrified wood. The jasper occurs in a variety of bright colors and patterns, making it highly desirable for cutting and polishing. The shores south of Buckhorn Campground, the head of Burris Creek, and much of the gravel and boulders lining Stony Creek for many miles to the south are especially productive. Carefully inspect all areas of erosion, especially at the mentioned locations. It takes some concentration to locate material from this locality, due to its frequently abraded exterior. The rounded, dull surface of the stones often conceals the vivid interior colors and patterns. For that reason, it is suggested that you closely examine any rocks displaying even the most pale color.

Fall and early winter seem to be the best collecting times, since the water level is usually low, thereby exposing more of the bank. The jasper is found in shades of yellow, orange, red, and green, with some containing showy inclusions of marcasite. Specimens range in size from boulders to pebbles, and a pick and shovel are handy for unearthing partially buried chunks.

The farther south along Stony Creek you go, the more abraded the material becomes and, therefore, the more difficult it is to find. In addition, many portions of Stony Creek are on private property, so it is essential that you first determine the collecting status of any spot you plan to explore. It is also suggested that you inquire at the Black Butte Reservoir headquarters to determine restricted areas and other limitations related to rockhounding within the Recreation Area boundaries.

If there are problems with collecting at the reservoir, an alternate site is illustrated on the map. To get there, head south toward Elk Grove to where the pavement crosses Stony Creek as shown on the map. At that point, some tracks will be seen heading east, paralleling the creek. Explore any portion that is **NOT ON PRIVATE PROPERTY**. As mentioned earlier, the jasper tends to be more abraded this far down, but, once cut and polished, it is as good as that obtained nearer the lake.

Searching for minerals alongside Stony Creek

STONY CREEK

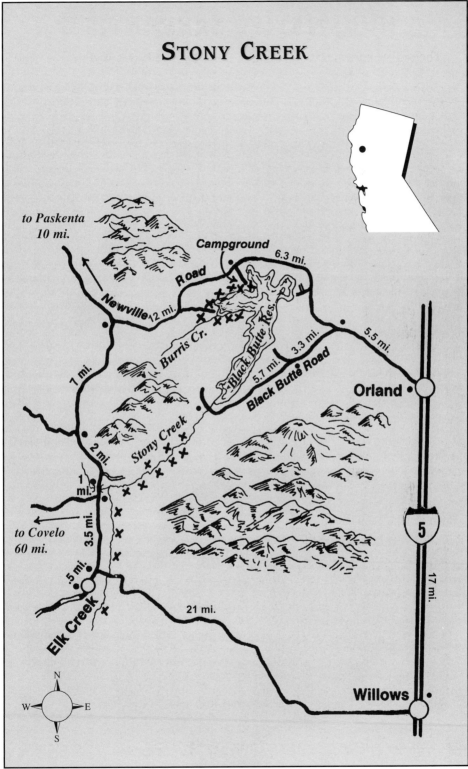

to Paskenta
10 mi.

Campground

6.3 mi.

Newville

Road

12 mi.

Burris Cr.

Black Butte Res.

5.7 mi.

3.3 mi.

Black Butte Road

5.5 mi.

Orland

7 mi.

2 mi.

Stony Creek

1 mi.

3.5 mi.

to Covelo
60 mi.

.5 mi.

Elk Creek

21 mi.

5

17 mi.

Willows

N
W   E
S

HIGHWAY 70 SERPENTINE

A huge amount of serpentine can be found in a series of roadcuts extending at least one mile along Highway 70, about 24 miles northeast of Oroville. To reach the start of this massive deposit, take Highway 70 approximately 18 miles northeast from where it intersects Highway 149. At the given mileage, you will find yourself passing through a "polished" greenish roadcut, the coloration due to its high serpentine content. Don't worry about not seeing it since the terrain and native rock radically change suddenly and the smooth, grayish-green, dull polished appearance of the serpentine is impossible to miss.

Be careful where you pull off the road along here, since this is a relatively well traveled stretch of highway. There are a number of turnouts, off the pavement, which are safe for parking. Be very careful when crossing, since motorists will not be expecting pedestrians.

The quality of what can be found here varies considerably. There is some excellent deep green material, but most occurs in combination with gray, white and black. Specimens showing all of these colors can be very desirable, so don't restrict your search to only pure green material. If pieces are solid enough, they can be used to make exquisite carvings, bookends, large cabochons, etc. As with most serpentine, however, much of it flakes and easily chips, making it very difficult to polish. With persistence and patience, though, it shouldn't be too difficult to get lots of good workable material.

If you are not satisfied with what can be found at your first stop, simply drive or walk a little farther and try again. Again, the color and quality changes quite a bit within these roadcuts. Look for regions with the most vivid green, since those tend to offer the best all-around specimens. **DO NOT** knock any stones onto the highway. If something accidentally rolls onto the pavement, remove it immediately. Again, be very careful when crossing the road and park safely!

A huge wall of serpentine in a road cut alongside Highway 70

HIGHWAY 70 SERPENTINE

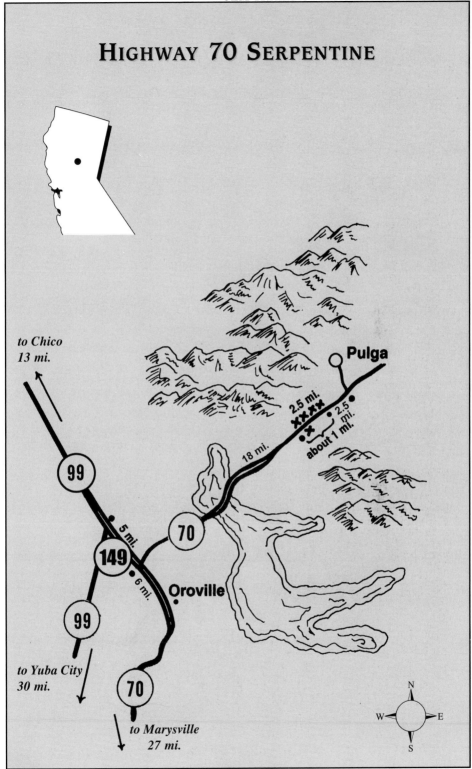

to Chico
13 mi.

Pulga

2.5 mi.
2.5 mi.
about 1 mi.

18 mi.

99

149

70

5 mi.

6 mi.

Oroville

99

to Yuba City
30 mi.

70

to Marysville
27 mi.

N
W E
S

PULGA

Beautiful apple-green vesuvianite (idocrase), serpentine, and some small garnet crystals can be found in the scenic region surrounding the small town of Pulga. Vesuvianite, often referred to as "California Jade," possesses properties very similar to jade and, for that reason, it is very desirable among lapidary craftsmen.

Site "A" is, by far, the most accessible of the Pulga locations. As shown on the map, it is located in a road cut just off Highway 70, on the way to town. There, it is possible to find lots of nice green serpentine, but you should be very careful to not allow any rocks to fall onto the pavement as you collect. Parking at Site "A" is also challenging. This is a narrow road, and in order not to block traffic, it might be necessary to pull off a short distance beyond and walk back.

Site "B" is far more demanding to get to, involving a steep one-mile hike, and should only be visited by collectors in excellent health. It boasts very nice apple-green vesuvianite, serpentine and small garnet crystals. To get there, continue along Pulga Road to where it intersects Camp Creek Road. It should be mentioned that, at this junction, occasional pieces of vesuvianite bearing rock can be found in the stream just below the bridge, and it might be worth a stop. The trail leading to Site "B" is just beyond that intersection, and is actually the unpaved extension of Camp Creek Road. The reason it must be hiked is due to extreme washouts along the way, so severe that even four-wheel drive units can't get very far. Rather than taking a chance of getting stuck, park out of the way and walk. The diggings are fairly easy to spot, occurring in the limestone near contact regions with igneous rock.

Search in the rubble below the diggings or attack the limestone with sledge hammer, gads and pry bars. The gem vesuvianite occurs as small nodules and lenses within the host rock. It takes a lot of work to extract large quantities, but the effort is usually rewarded.

Site "C" is located behind a highway maintenance station, and is reached by hiking up a *steep* trail past an Indian burial ground. There is a rough road, about 0.1 miles east of the maintenance yard, which intersects that trail. Park in a safe place across the highway and walk from there. The occurrence is similar to that at Site "B", and should be explored in a similar manner. Be sure to spend some time looking through the gravel and boulders lining Mill Creek for additional specimens.

PULGA

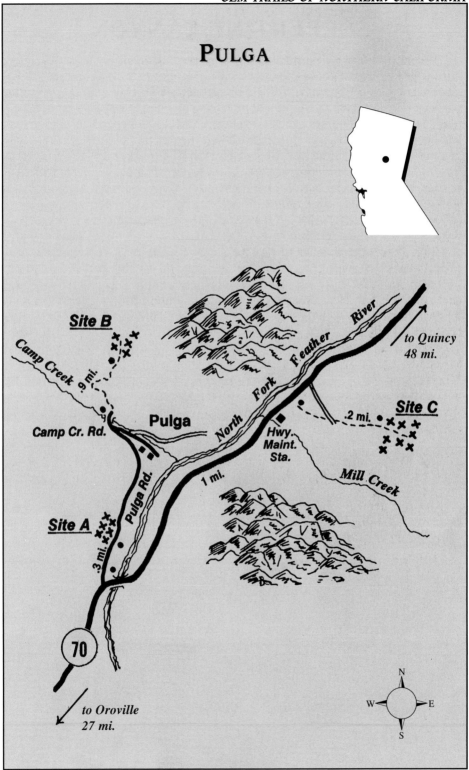

SERPENTINE CANYON

This is a sizable collecting area, actually encompassing numerous roadcuts throughout famous Serpentine Canyon. The locality is most easily reached by heading west on Highway 70 from where it meets Highway 89, about 11 miles north of Quincy. From there, go about 10 miles and you will find yourself virtually surrounded by light green serpentine. Park anywhere along this stretch, but be very careful where you pull off the pavement, since it is a relatively busy roadway and motorists will not be expecting parked or extremely slow moving vehicles. There are a number of turnouts, off the pavement, which are safe for parking, so be sure to use them. In addition, be most cautious when walking on the road, since motorists will not be expecting pedestrians.

The collecting continues at least four more miles along the highway, and the quality varies considerably, making it necessary to take enough time to properly inspect the site. There is some excellent deep green material, but most is in combination with gray, white and black. Solid specimens can be used by craftsmen to make exquisite carvings, bookends, large cabochons, and other lapidary items. As is the case with most serpentine, however, there is lots of flaky material here, making it necessary to exhibit patience in order to find the best available.

If you are not satisfied with what you find at your first stop, simply drive or walk a little farther and try again. The color changes quite a bit within this deposit, and that is very noticeable, even when driving on the highway. **DO NOT** knock any stones onto the road. If something does accidentally roll onto the pavement, remove it immediately. Again, be very careful when crossing and park safely.

SERPENTINE CANYON

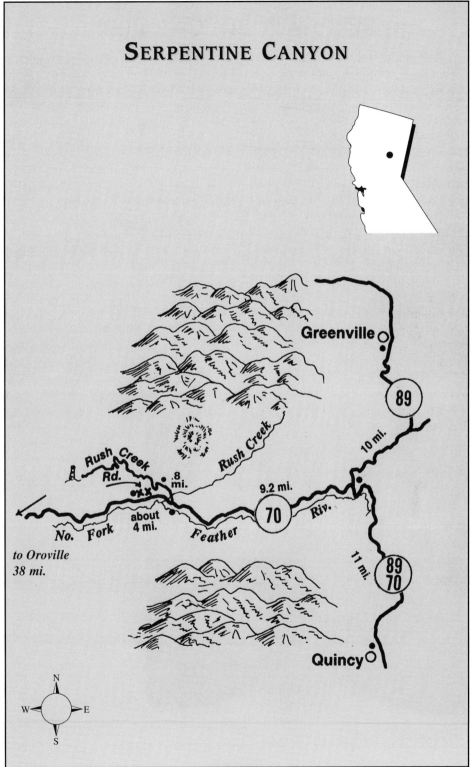

Greenville

89

10 mi.

Rush Creek
Rd.

Rush Creek

.8
mi.

9.2 mi.

70

Riv.

No.   Fork

about
4 mi.

Feather

to Oroville
38 mi.

11 mi.

89
70

Quincy

N
W   E
S

LA PORTE

The Upper Dutch Diggings, north of La Porte, provide collectors with an opportunity to gather some nice Middle Oligocene fossil leaves. The fossils occur in a solidified volcanic ash resting upon the famous gold bearing gravels which brought prospectors to this region in the first place. In fact, the leaves were first discovered by miners, when examining their hydraulically "cleaned" cliffs.

To get to there, take Highway E-21 northeast from Highway 20 to La Porte, a drive of about 46 miles. In town, turn left onto Aristocracy Drive, which is somewhat difficult to spot. Go north, following Aristocracy Drive as it makes a sharp left turn. One-tenth of a mile from Road E-21 is an intersection. Aristocracy Drive veers right, but you should bear straight ahead onto Primeau Drive. The pavement ends shortly afterward, and the road goes right, crosses a little wooden bridge, and then continues to the north. After having gone about 0.8 miles from Aristocracy Drive, rough tracks will be encountered heading to the right, alongside the Lower Dutch Diggings. This short drive is very interesting, going right through the remnants of the massive hydraulic gold mining which took place about 150 years ago.

It will probably be necessary to park where the tracks intersect, even if you have a four-wheel drive vehicle, but the walk through the Lower Dutch Diggings is easy and interesting. Hike to the east, over the little greenish colored ridge, about 0.3 miles to the Upper Dutch Diggings. Then, follow the overgrown gully, closest to the cliffs on the north, and carefully split any of the greenish, blocky, fossil bearing tuff that you encounter. The fossil rock is fairly

easy to distinguish from other stones in the region, due to its distinctive color. The most productive collecting is done by splitting and then carefully examining that light green material, hoping to expose an otherwise hidden leaf. Remember that the fossils are fragile, so protect them for the trek back to where you parked.

Road leading to La Porte collecting site

LA PORTE

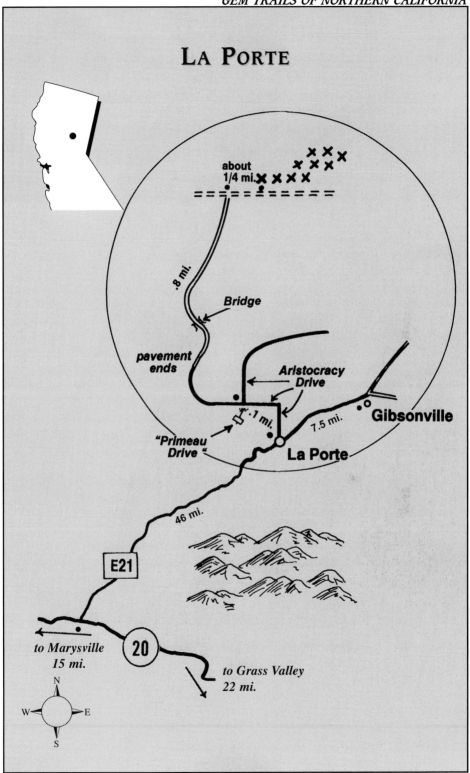

about 1/4 mi.

.8 mi.

Bridge

pavement ends

Aristocracy Drive

"Primeau Drive "

.1 mi.

7.5 mi.

Gibsonville

La Porte

46 mi.

E21

20

to Marysville 15 mi.

to Grass Valley 22 mi.

N
W E
S

GOLD VALLEY

This is a four-wheel drive location, of interest only to rockhounds with a sense of adventure and a desire to do some exploration. Pyrite is the primary mineral of interest and some is found in association with gold, just to add a little excitement to the search. The pyrite crystals are often distinct cubes, occasionally measuring up to one-quarter of an inch across, and often make nice display pieces.

To get to Gold Valley, go about ten miles west on Highway 49, from where it intersects Highway 89, just past the tiny town of Bassetts. If coming from the west, this turnoff is six miles east of Sierra City. Turn north on the road to Graeagle, proceed about seven miles, and just before reaching Gold Lake, turn left onto the tracks running along the southern shore. After passing the lake and going about six miles you will be in the south of Gold Valley. The last few miles of this trip goes over some very rough stretches of road. Do not attempt getting through in a passenger car. High clearance and probably four-wheel drive are essential. At the given mileage, go right into Gold Valley, toward Hawley Lake, approximately two miles farther. Search any of the abandoned mine dumps along this final stretch, as well as any areas of erosion, especially along the banks of Pauley Creek, which runs through the center of Gold Valley.

Rock containing the crystals will most likely be very tarnished and, therefore, difficult to spot. Look for off-white, yellowish, or black/brown rock and split it in hopes of exposing sparkling, golden, pyrite. When you find a good piece, save it until you return home to better clean and trim it for display.

While in the area, it is suggested that you continue to Downieville, about fifteen miles west of Bassetts, along Highway 49. This is an interesting gold rush town, and it is reported that quartz crystals and green copper ore, frequently filled with tiny, sparkling pyrite crystals, can be found along the roads of Ruby Mountain, especially those near the Ruby Mine, just southwest of town. Inquire at the Ranger Station in Downieville for information regarding current road conditions before setting out. It should also be mentioned that there are lots of nice serpentine and pyrite bearing rocks to be found in most of the riverbeds and banks in and around Downieville.

GOLD VALLEY

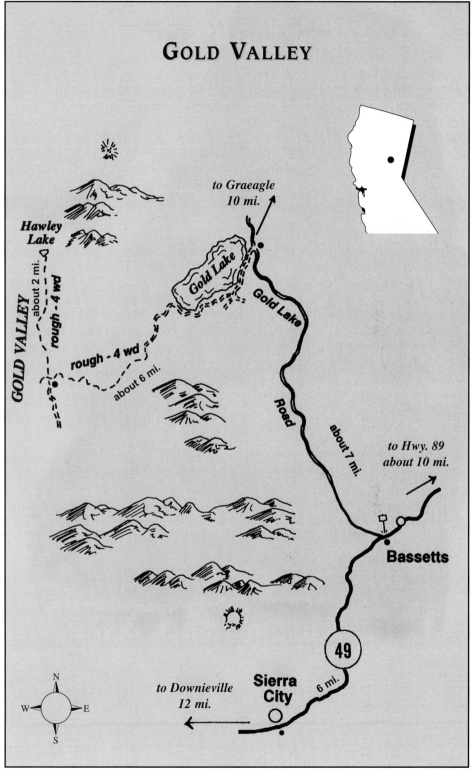

Hawley
Lake

about 2 mi.

rough - 4 wd

GOLD VALLEY

rough - 4 wd

about 6 mi.

Gold Lake

*to Graeagle
10 mi.*

Gold Lake

Road

about 7 mi.

*to Hwy. 89
about 10 mi.*

Bassetts

49

**Sierra
City**

6 mi.

*to Downieville
12 mi.*

N
W E
S

GOODYEAR'S BAR

Good quality serpentine can be found throughout the scenic region surrounding Goodyear's Bar, situated alongside the North Yuba River. The most accessible of the deposits is Serpentine Hill, a tiny mountain composed entirely of that colorful green mineral. To get there, travel west from Downieville 4.4 miles to the Goodyear's Bar Road turnoff. As you approach, there is a large roadcut, on the north, composed entirely of serpentine, and just before the turn, on the south, is Serpentine Hill.

There is a good flat area upon which to park between Goodyear's Bar Road and the hill, and it is suggested that you base your collecting from there. You can inspect the hill, cross the highway to see if there is anything better in the roadcut, or walk down Goodyear's Bar Road and examine some of the other deposits near the bridge and along the river.

If you choose to collect in the roadcuts alongside Highway 49 or Goodyear's Bar Road, be sure you do not knock any stones onto the pavement. If something accidentally gets onto the roadway, immediately remove it, since it could be a hazard to traffic. Be very careful when crossing the roads, since cars move quite fast through here, and drivers are not expecting to encounter pedestrians.

There is lots of nice specimen grade serpentine in this area some with an intense green hue. Much, though, is somewhat flaky, thereby being difficult to cut and polish. There is some solid material, but it takes patience and perseverance to locate. In addition to the near solid shades of green, there is also some mottled material containing green, white and gray. Some specimens are filled with interesting black inclusions. Solid pieces, showing all the different colors, are highly prized by craftsmen for use in a multitude of applications.

Bright green serpentine roadcut at Goodyear's Bar

GOODYEAR'S BAR

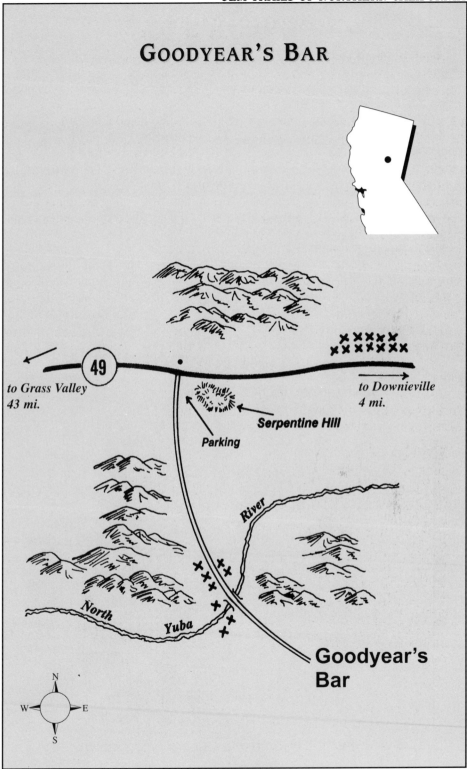

to Grass Valley
43 mi.

49

to Downieville
4 mi.

Serpentine Hill

Parking

River

North   *Yuba*

**Goodyear's
Bar**

N
W — E
S

BABCOCK PEAK

Beautiful pink and occasionally near-red quartz can be found on the slopes of Babcock Peak, about 37 miles northeast of Taylorsville. Much of what can be found can be used for making cabochons, faceted stones and countless larger items such as bookends and spheres.

The accompanying map shows three locations where the rose quartz can be found. Two are in and around Last Chance Creek, and the third is on the slopes of Babcock Peak. The latter two locations involve traveling on some rough roads, but four-wheel drive is generally not needed unless there has been some severe weather shortly before your visit.

The route to these spots takes you through some scenic terrain, and a stop for a few nights at nearby Antelope Lake makes the locality even more appealing. To get there, start in Taylorsville and take Antelope Lake Road, which is County Road 112, about eight miles to where it heads south and Country Road 111 continues another 17 miles to the lake. When you enter the National Forest, the road also becomes Forest Road 172. Continue following Forest Road 172 (which now also becomes Forest Road 28N03) as it skirts the southern edge of Antelope Lake for 3.2 miles. Forest Road 28N03 then heads southeast and you should proceed another two miles to where Forest Road 26N07 intersects on the right. From that point, Site #1 is reached by continuing on Forest Road 28N03 another 3.2 miles to Murdock Crossing. Park there and look in and around the creek for chunks and pebbles of the rose quartz. Don't hesitate to do some walking in either direction along the creek.

To get to Sites #2 and #3, take the right fork at the above intersection onto Forest Road 26N07 and go 4.9 miles to where it meets Forest Road 26N46, just next to Last Chance Creek, which is Site #2. Collect in and around the creek as you did at Site #1. To get to Site #3, one of the primary rose quartz sources, go another 2.2 miles on Forest Road 26N46 and bear right toward Babcock Peak, stopping anywhere you spot something of interest. The most prolific deposit which, at one time was a mining claim, is accessed by going about 0.8 miles on Forest Road 26N99, as illustrated on the map, and parking where the washed out tracks lead to the obvious quartz deposits up the hill. Hike that short distance and either pick up material that has already been broken loose, or attack the tough quartz with hard rock tools including chisels, gads and a sledge hammer. Be sure to wear goggles and gloves since the quartz shatters into sharp fragments when struck. It is also at Site #3 where the beautiful, almost red quartz can be found.

BABCOCK PEAK

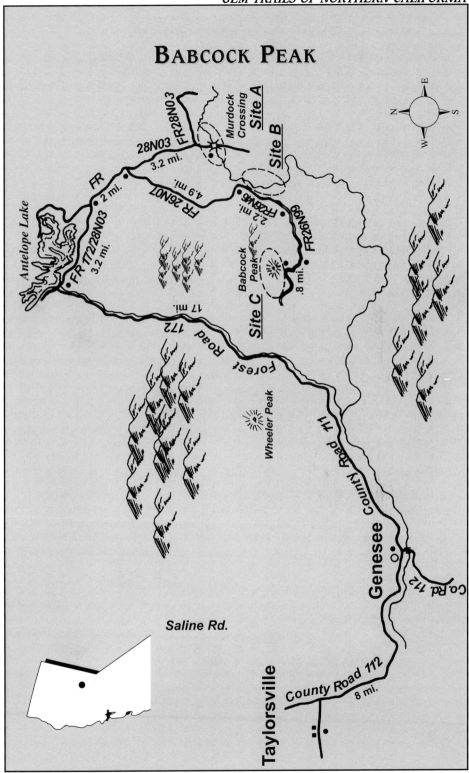

TAYLORSVILLE

Interesting fossil shell impressions can be found within a deposit of green and red shale a short distance east of Taylorsville. To get there, follow Taylorsville Road (A-22) to town, approximately four miles east from where it intersects Highway 89. Continue east 0.4 miles to the Taylorsville Park and Campground, where you should go left. About 0.1 miles farther there is a metal gate and some ruts leading off to the west, as shown on the map. The collecting site is on the hillside directly opposite those ruts. There aren't too many good places to pull off the pavement around here, but a few cars can probably squeeze in at the clearing near the gate. Another possibility is to pull into the Taylorsville Park, and walk the short distance back up the road. In any event, whatever you decide to do, be certain that you don't block the road and be careful when crossing.

The collecting is done just about anywhere within the reddish and greenish shale seen on the cliffs for at least 0.25 miles. To locate the impressions break pieces directly from the hillside and split along the bedding planes with a small chisel and hammer. If you don't feel like directly attacking the primary deposit, look through the tons of already loosened chunks littering the lower mountainside which actually tends to be the most productive and less strenuous method. Just sit among the rubble and randomly examine the shale for signs of the shell casts. If you find something which is only partially exposed, save it for later when you can carefully finish splitting it along the bedding plane with a small sharp knife, an awl, or an ice pick.

This is a most pleasant collecting spot and it is extremely difficult to imagine it to have once been at the bottom of a lake. The fascinating impressions left by the now dissolved shells, however, offer proof that this indeed was the case. The shells originate from the Cenozoic period, and the entire slope is covered with the conspicuously colored, fossil bearing shale. Be advised that this is primarily a summer location, since it gets very cold during the winter.

A view of the Taylorsville site from the road

TAYLORSVILLE

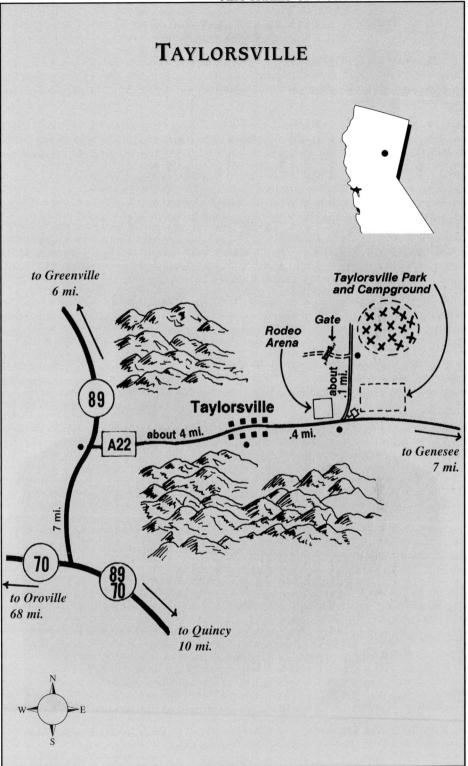

to Greenville
6 mi.

Taylorsville Park
and Campground

Rodeo
Arena

Gate

89

A22   about 4 mi.

Taylorsville

about .1 mi.

.4 mi.

to Genesee
7 mi.

7 mi.

70

89
70

to Oroville
68 mi.

to Quincy
10 mi.

N
W   E
S

HALLELUJAH MOUNTAIN

Hallelujah Mountain, designated as Site "A", has been a highly regarded collecting spot for years. It boasts smoky citrine, amethyst, milky and water-clear quartz crystals, some of which are rare scepter varieties. The crystals are found lining cavities in the local rock, or loose in the soil of the lower slopes and washes. The most ambitious collecting method entails use of a sledge hammer, gads and/or chisels to split the rocks in hopes of opening a crystal-bearing cavity. This is exhausting work, but offers lots of potential. You can look for crystal bearing seams on the rocky ledges, high on the mountain, or in any of the boulders farther down.

There is a faint trail, which can be spotted from the suggested parking area shown on the map, leading to the most productive areas. The hike isn't too bad, and the view is spectacular. For those not wanting to do strenuous hiking or heavy sledge work, good specimens can often be found by closely examining boulders and rocks in lower areas and/or screening the soil in the foothill washes. Be sure to close the highway gate after driving through.

Site "B" is only a short distance south of Hallelujah Mountain and offers rockhounds an opportunity to gather colorful jasper and occasional chunks of agate and petrified wood. Nothing is plentiful, but the quality helps to make up for that deficiency. Start at the telephone lines and continue east for quite a distance. Look everywhere, especially in areas of erosion. The jasper is generally in solid tones of red, yellow and orange, while the agate is primarily dark, with occasional interesting inclusions. This is a vast site, so plan to do some walking. Most of what can be found is small, but every now and then large chunks can be picked up. Once again, be sure to close the highway gate after you pass through.

Searching the lowlands for quartz crystals at Hallelujah Mountain

HALLELUJAH MOUNTAIN

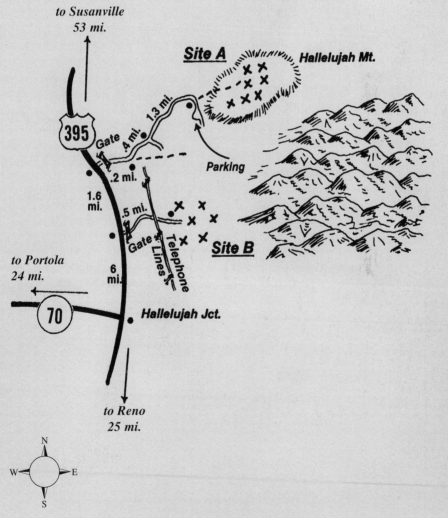

to Susanville
53 mi.

Site A

Hallelujah Mt.

395

1.3 mi.

Gate

.4 mi.

Parking

.2 mi.

1.6
mi.

.5 ml.

Gate

Telephone
Lines

Site B

to Portola
24 mi.

6
mi.

70

Hallelujah Jct.

to Reno
25 mi.

N
W   E
S

KELSEYVILLE

Quality obsidian and sporadic pieces of colorful jasper can be picked up throughout the countryside just south of Kelseyville, especially at the three sites shown on the map.

To get to Site "A", head south on Highway 175 from Kelseyville 3.4 miles and bear right onto Bottle Rock Road. Continue about one more mile to the center of one of many fine obsidian fields in this highly volcanic region. There are numerous places to turn off the pavement all along Bottle Rock Road for quite a distance, and each of these turnouts affords good collecting potential.

The obsidian is sometimes difficult to spot, since it frequently is disguised with a pitted, reddish-brown crust, but splitting any suspect stone with a rock pick makes identification easy. Be sure as you split rocks, to wear a good pair of goggles. Razor sharp glass splinters are sent flying through the air when struck, and if they get in your eye there could be a serious problem! Much of what can be found here is good quality, some being faceting grade, with the primary color being black. A few pieces of mahogany and swirled material also can be procured, as can occasional snowflake specimens. Size ranges from tiny pebbles to large boulders. It isn't necessary to do any digging, since so much can be found on the surface. Just walk through the brush, keeping a keen eye on the ground. Be advised that there is lots of private land in the area, so don't cross any fences to collect. There is more than enough on public land.

Site "B" is a little less accessible, but offers some additional collecting in this most pleasant region. To get there, take Bell Hill Road 3.6 miles from town and then turn left onto Adobe Creek Road, proceeding another 1.7 miles. At that point, the road starts to parallel Adobe Creek. All along the banks of the creek, for quite a distance in both directions, rockhounds can find obsidian, a good selection of colorful jasper, and green serpentine. Tracks will be encountered leading to the little stream all along Adobe Creek Road. Be sure to stay off private property.

Site "C" offers more obsidian, and it should be noted that many of the local roadcuts contain a very good quality of green serpentine, so be on the lookout!

Parked at Kelseyville, Site A

KELSEYVILLE

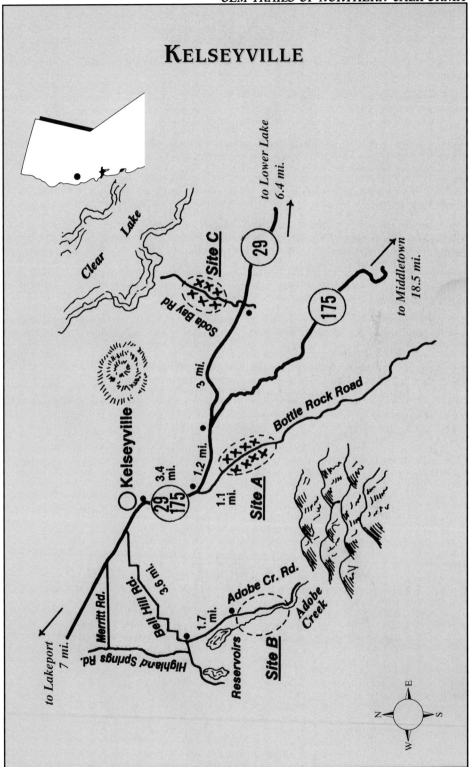

CLEAR LAKE

The hills and valleys south of Clear Lake offer some tiny mineralogical oddities, often referred to as Lake County Diamonds. These glasslike quartz pebbles are unusual in that they do not show any crystal faces, and are generally water clear. Due to their hardness and near flawlessness, they have been prized by faceters for years. Most of them are small, generally measuring less than one inch in length, but the quality more than makes up for what is lacking in size. The tiny crystals are, for the most part, colorless, but occasionally specimens exhibiting pale shades of purple, orange, smoke, blue, or pink are encountered. These colored varieties are often spectacular when faceted.

Simply follow the instructions on the map to get to Site "A", the center of the Lake County Diamond collecting area. It is important to note that a major problem associated with exploring this area is the abundance of private land. **DO NOT**, under any circumstances, be tempted to cross through fences without first gaining authorization to do so. If you are hesitant to seek permission to search on private land, try a careful examination of regions immediately adjacent to the road or in unfenced and unposted places.

The best time to visit is shortly after the fields have been plowed or following a good rain. Screening the soil in the dry creek beds often proves fruitful, as does gently turning the surface soil with a small hand rake. The most popular method of collecting here, however, is to simply walk through the brush looking for a flash caused by sunlight hitting the glasslike gems.

Site "B" provides collectors with colorful jasper, interesting fossils, and even the chance of coming upon an Indian artifact. To get there, go north from Lower Lake on Highway 53 for 7.5 miles, and then proceed east on Highway 20 another 5.5 miles. At that point, the highway meets the north fork of Cache Creek. Park well off the pavement and hike north along that waterway to conduct your search.

CLEAR LAKE

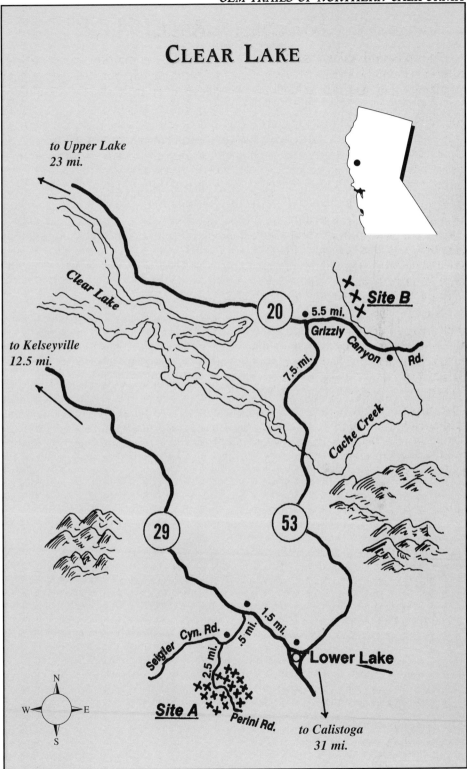

to Upper Lake
23 mi.

Clear Lake

to Kelseyville
12.5 mi.

20

5.5 mi.

Grizzly Canyon Rd.

Site B

7.5 mi.

Cache Creek

29

53

1.5 mi.

Seigler Cyn. Rd.

.5 mi.

2.5 mi.

Lower Lake

Site A

Perini Rd.

to Calistoga
31 mi.

N
W   E
S

CALIFORNIA PETRIFIED FOREST

This location, known as California's Petrified Forest, provides an opportunity to see what remains of a redwood forest that existed here over 3 million years ago. It is imperative to emphasize that this is **not** a collecting site, but it is a fascinating place to visit and should be of interest to most mineral collectors. A fee is charged to tour the "forest" and, at time of publication, it is $6.00 for adults, $5.00 for seniors over 60, and $3.00 for children. Specimens are available for purchase in the souvenir shop if you want something to take home for your collection.

The silicified trees found here were originally buried in volcanic ash during a period of seismic activity which lasted, periodically, about one million years. As this was happening, water filtered through the soil and rock, slowly replacing the rotting trees with silica, cell by cell, molecule by molecule, to form solid quartz replicas.

During the next approximately one million years, eastward pressures along the San Andreas Fault caused massive uplifts forming the Coast Mountain Range. That process allowed streams and rivers to erode into the ancient volcanic deposits and expose the long hidden, and now petrified, forest which once stood in this region.

To get there from Calistoga, situated on Highway 128 a short distance north of the famous Napa Valley wine region, take Petrified Forest Road 4.7 miles southwest toward Santa Rosa to the entrance. It is open from 9 AM until 5 PM (6 PM in the summer). There are hiking trails throughout the site, and most are accessible to wheelchairs. For more information, write to 4100 Petrified Forest Road, Calistoga, CA 94515, or e-mail: manager@petrifiedforest.org, or call (707) 942-6667, or check their website: http://www.petrifiedforest.org.

While in the area, stop by California's Old Faithful Geyser, which erupts regularly about every 40 minutes. It is located just north of town.

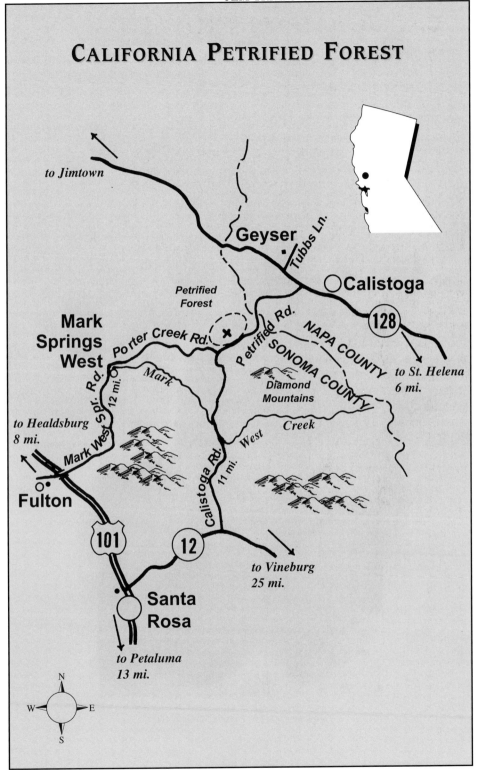

CALIFORNIA PETRIFIED FOREST

to Jimtown

Geyser

Tubbs Ln.

Calistoga

Petrified
Forest

Mark
Springs
West

Porter Creek Rd.

Petrified Rd.

NAPA COUNTY

SONOMA COUNTY

128

to St. Helena
6 mi.

Mark

Diamond
Mountains

Mark West Spr. Rd.

12 mi.

to Healdsburg
8 mi.

West

Creek

Fulton

Calistoga Rd.

11 mi.

101

12

to Vineburg
25 mi.

Santa
Rosa

to Petaluma
13 mi.

N
W   E
S

CHALK BLUFF

One of the best places in all of California to find fossilized plants is not too far from Colfax, and well worth the trip. To get to this fascinating location, follow Highway 174 north from Colfax 7.5 miles from where it intersects Interstate 80. Go east on You Bet Road 4.5 miles, then bear left onto Red Dog Road another 1.8 miles. At that point, there are some unmarked tracks heading off to the right, and it is there where you should turn and go another 0.6 miles to a wide area in the road upon which you can pull off.

Within the banks directly below the road are embedded an incredible variety of extremely well preserved Middle Eocene plant fossils, as well as some nice petrified wood. The best collecting is done north of the road in the grayish clay, at the base of the canyon. The lowlands, on all sides, are filled with conspicuous mud hills left from the gold rush days when this entire region was hydraulically mined. These remnants of the controversial hydraulic mining era can be seen throughout the landscape for many miles in all directions, reminding us of the days when the area supplied millions of dollars in gold.

To get to the fossil areas, carefully hike down to the low-lying regions. The trek is very steep, and care should be taken to make sure you find a safe place to descend. Very close to where you park, there are some tracks heading down, and it is advised that you use them. Do not attempt driving, since getting back out, even with four-wheel drive, is most treacherous.

Once down, examine the gray clay strata, primarily on the southern side of the canyon below the road. The fossil bearing region is about four or five feet thick, and easy to distinguish, due to its color contrasting against the brown, pebble filled surrounding soils. Once at the fossil zone, chip off a sample and chances are very high it will contain some fossilized leaves and twigs. If not, just keep trying.

A view of the Chalk Bluff site

CHALK BLUFF

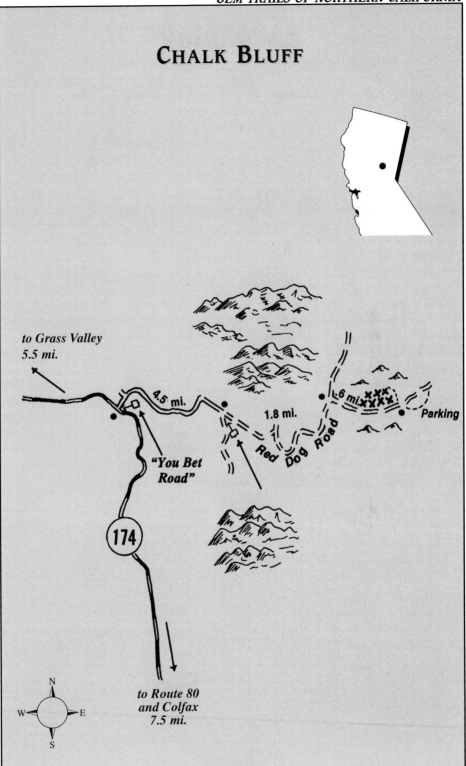

to Grass Valley
5.5 mi.

4.5 mi.

1.8 mi.

.6 mi.

Parking

Red Dog Road

"You Bet Road"

174

N
W E
S

to Route 80
and Colfax
7.5 mi.

CRYSTAL PEAK

Getting nicely terminated quartz crystals from these two locations requires driving about ten miles on a sometimes steep but generally well-graded dirt road, hiking and working at over 7,000 feet, and also having a certain amount of luck. It is a beautiful place to spend some time, however, so if you are the adventurous type, these locations are for you. As enticement, it should be mentioned that well formed crystals measuring over one foot in length have been found here, even though the average seems to be only a couple of inches.

To get to both spots, start in Verdi, Nevada, just east of the state line. Go north on Dog Valley Road, and then onto Long Valley Road, as they tend northward to Dog Valley Campground, about 5.5 miles from Verdi. From there, you can either continue northward to the Babbitt Peak location, which is the most accessible and most productive of the two, or you can follow the somewhat steep and rough road illustrated on the map five miles, or as far as you can go, into the foothills of Crystal Peak. If you visit the road's end Crystal Peak location, roam through the lowlands carefully scrutinizing the ground for crystals and/or try to find crystal bearing pockets within the rocky areas. If you want to get crystals out of those pockets, however, hard rock tools such as a hand sledge, gads and chisels, accompanied by lots of hard work, will be needed. Goggles and gloves are also essential equipment items for busting up and into the tough host rock.

To get to the Babbitt Peak location, which actually should be your first stop so you can get a good idea as to exactly what type of native rock contains the crystal pockets, continue on the main road another four miles to where another road intersects from the west. That road goes past an old gate to a long abandoned quartz mine about one-half mile away. Be advised that it is very rough and a high clearance four-wheel drive unit might be needed to go the entire distance. If you do not have such a vehicle, just park and hike, keeping an eye out, as you go, for crystals on the ground.

Diggings will easily be seen throughout the almost barren, grayish, rocky regions in the vicinity of the old mining operation. Use the pits and holes where previous collectors have been working as a starting point and, as at Crystal Peak, either continue breaking into the tough encasing rock with hard rock tools or carefully examine the rubble already broken loose down below.

CRYSTAL PEAK

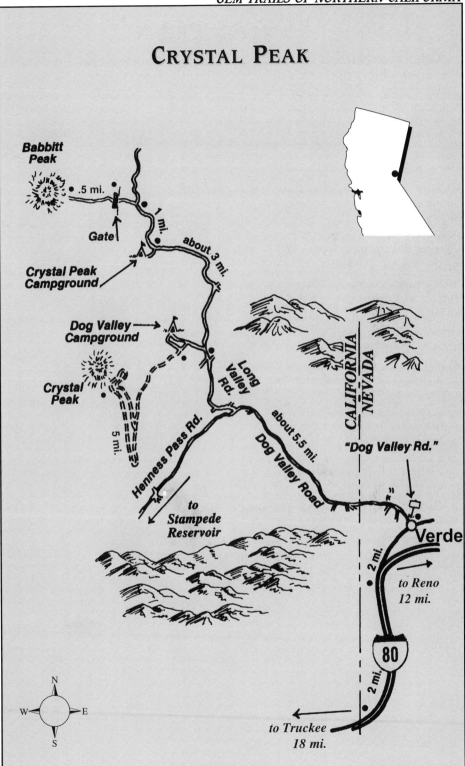

Babbitt Peak

.5 mi.

1 mi.

Gate

about 3 mi.

Crystal Peak Campground

Dog Valley Campground

Long Valley Rd.

Crystal Peak

CALIFORNIA

NEVADA

Henness Pass Rd.

5 mi.

Dog Valley Road

about 5.5 mi.

"Dog Valley Rd."

to Stampede Reservoir

Verde

2 mi.

to Reno 12 mi.

80

2 mi.

to Truckee 18 mi.

N
W E
S

UNION FLAT

The Union Flat Casual Mining Area offers a nice half-mile stretch of the North Yuba River to try your luck at gold panning and, if you have a permit and a dredge, small scale dredge work is also allowed. The site has provided patient "prospectors" some nice flakes of gold over the years and is supervised by the U. S. Forest Service. If you want to obtain a dredge permit, contact the California Department of Fish and Game, License and Revenue Branch, 3211 S Street, Sacramento CA 95816, (916) 227-2245. The cost for the permit is $37.50 for a California resident and $147.25 for nonresidents. Before you go, if not familiar with gold panning techniques, be sure to get a good book on the subject. Such a purchase might just pay off many times over.

To get to the Union Flat Campground, take Highway 49 6.5 miles east from Downieville or 5.5 miles west from Sierra City. You can camp in the campground, but not in the nearby open forest, and there is a 14-day limit governing how long you can stay. Visitors can pan year-round, but there are specific regulations governing when you can use a dredge. In addition, you can only explore wet areas of the stream and are not allowed to break down the banks or uproot any plants or shrubs. Only hand tools can be used and you can't build little dams to trap flowing gold.

After each winter season the snow melt and heavy rainstorms seem to wash more gold into the river from the gold-bearing Tertiary deposits upstream. For more information about Union Flat and other nearby camping areas, contact the Tahoe National Forest, (530) 265-4531.

UNION FLAT

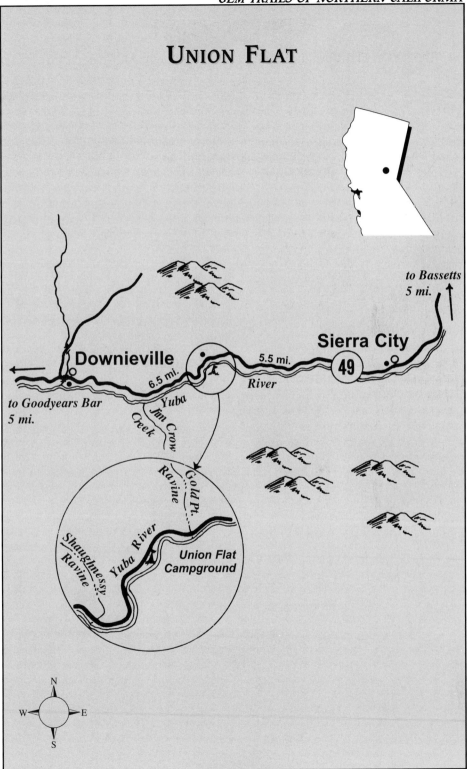

VIRGINIA CITY

Delicate leaf fossils can be found southeast of Reno, Nevada, just across the state line near historic Virginia City. To get from Reno to the collecting site, go south on Highway 395 about 11 miles then bear left onto Highway 341, toward Virginia City. Continue 11.5 miles to where a dirt road will intersect on the left. Turn left onto the dirt road. Keep in mind that Highway 341 is well traveled, making it essential that you properly signal your impending turn and that you are wary of high-speed oncoming traffic.

The difficulty in finding the fossil site is that there are so many intersecting roads from this point. Try to stay on the main road, and you should get to the little chalky diatomite hills containing the Lower Pliocene, 10 million year old leaves, with little or no difficulty. For the most part, you bear **right** at all **MAJOR** forks, traveling a total distance of approximately 6.5 miles. The road ends at the fossil bearing diatomite, better known as Chalk Hills. Simply break out a chunk of the relatively soft rock with a rock pick and then examine it for traces of the faint orange or brown fossils. If you find nothing on the first attempt, carefully split it again, and continue splitting until something turns up. If you find nothing in the first chunk of diatomite, remove another chunk and do it all over again.

The fossils are often very difficult to spot, since the bright white host material is very reflective and the subtle orange and brown fossils do not stand out particularly well. In fact, many of them appear more like casts or impressions rather than actual fossils. They do, however, make interesting display pieces, if you can find pieces with many leaves, all displayed in the same plane. Use a small, sharp knife or awl to carefully clean up anything you find. This is an arid region, so take plenty of water especially if you visit during the summer months.

VIRGINIA CITY

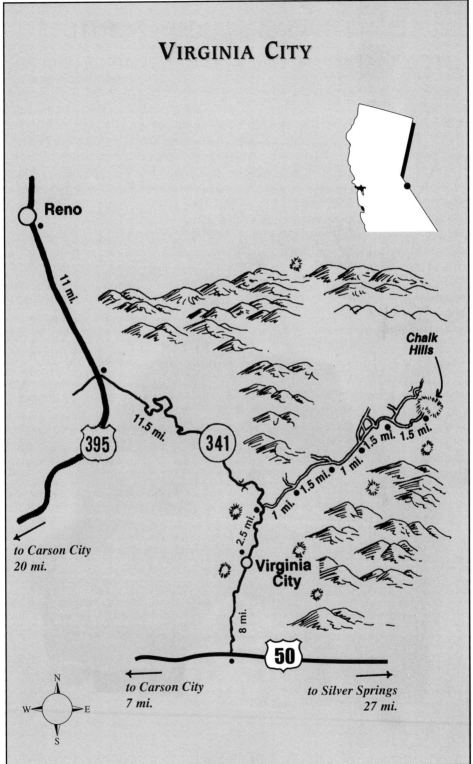

Reno

11 mi.

11.5 mi.

395

341

Chalk
Hills

1.5 mi.   1.5 mi.

1.5 mi.   1 mi.

1 mi.

2.5 mi.

to Carson City
20 mi.

Virginia
City

8 mi.

50

to Carson City
7 mi.

to Silver Springs
27 mi.

N
W   E
S

GOLD RUSH COUNTRY - NORTH

Probably no other part of California has so much mineralogical fame as the Gold Rush Country. In terms of mineral collecting, the region offers an incredible variety, including agate, jasper, marble, opal, fossils, soapstone, serpentine, gold, silver, calcite, garnet, pyrite, chalcopyrite, mica, chromium, mariposite, jade, epidote, vesuvianite, quartz crystals, and much more. There is so much private property throughout here, though, that it is often difficult to access any good collecting sites. As you drive to some or all of the spots shown on the accompanying map, search any abandoned mine dumps you might come upon, or inquire locally for suggestions. Even if you don't choose to search for minerals, a drive through this well known part of the country is both scenic and extremely interesting.

Downieville has a fascinating museum which provides lots of information about the rich mining that was done throughout the surrounding hills. At **Malakoff Diggins State Park**, visitors can view the effects of massive hydraulic mining. It is intriguing to see how the high pressure water simply reduced the hills to piles of debris, removing virtually all vegetation. In **Nevada City**, you can spend days roaming the museums and old sections of town. This was one of the centers of the Gold Rush, and a fascinating place to see. Be sure to view Firehouse #1 and the National Hotel, both built over 150 years ago.

Grass Valley is filled with antique shops and features the Empire Mine State Historic Park, which was one of the most productive of all the gold rush prospects. See also the Bourne Mansion, the mining museum at the North Star Mine water wheel, and the Gold Discovery Monument. **Coloma** boasts Gold Discovery Sate Park and the site of Sutter's Mill. The town itself has an interesting museum, antiques, and lots of interesting shops. **Washington** is nestled in a canyon along the South Yuba River and is most picturesque, appearing much like it did over 100 year ago. The Alpha and Omega Mines are in the hills nearby, both having been massive producers of gold through the turn of the twentieth century.

Gold Rush town of Coloma

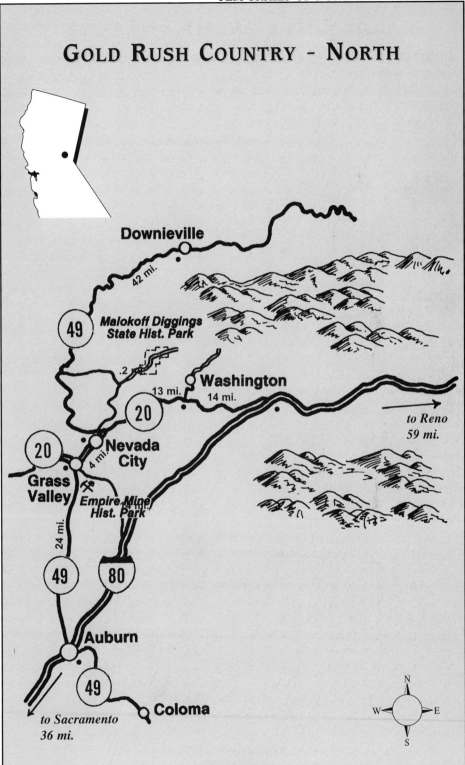

GOLD RUSH COUNTRY - NORTH

Downieville

42 mi.

49

*Malokoff Diggings
State Hist. Park*

.2

13 mi.

Washington

14 mi.

20

to Reno
59 mi.

20

Nevada
City

4 mi.

Grass
Valley

*Empire Mine
Hist. Park*

24 mi.

49   **80**

Auburn

49

to Sacramento
36 mi.

Coloma

N
W — E
S

TRAVERSE CREEK

The list of what can be found at this most productive site is extensive. There is chalcedony, epidote, serpentine, rose quartz, idocrase, jade, psilomelane, asbestos, massive grossular garnet, quartz crystals, and, occasionally, tiny and colorful vesuvianite crystals.

If you want to visit Traverse Creek Special Interest Area, which at one time was called the Stifle Memorial Claims, go two miles north from Placerville on Highway 49, bear right onto Highway 193 another 11.2 miles, then turn right onto Meadowbrook Road. Go another 1.3 miles and then right onto Bear Creek Road, crossing the little stream to the designated parking area. This site consists of what were once a series of adjacent private claims, but all are now open to rockhounds and administered by the U.S. Department of Agriculture–Forestry Service. At time of publication, no fee was charged or permit required to collect at Traverse Creek.

Much of what can be found here must be removed from host rock using tools such as rock picks, gads, chisels and hand sledges, as well as goggles and gloves. It is necessary to break into crystal bearing regions and then carefully remove the little gems and/or manageable portions of the host rock with the crystals still attached. If you don't choose to engage in such labor there is still plenty to be found by searching through the debris at any of the four claims and the surrounding terrain.

The vesuvianite crystals are quite small, usually measuring less than 1/8 inch in length, but they are a beautiful bright green color. The grossularite is massive and suitable for cutting, but faceting grade material is not readily available. The serpentine is colorful and looks much like low-grade jade, but it is generally flaky and can be used for nothing more than display, as is. The idocrase is white, mottled with regions of light green. Additional information can be obtained by writing to the El Dorado County Mineral and Gem Society, PO Box 950, Placerville, CA 95667.

TRAVERSE CREEK

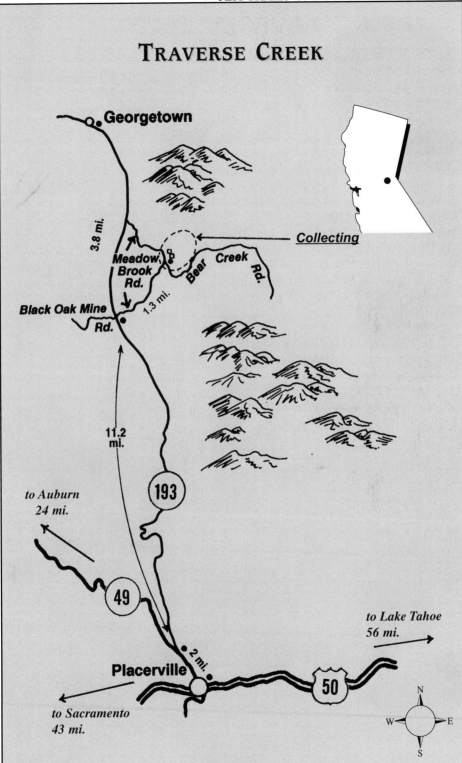

FOLSOM LAKE

The region surrounding Folsom Lake, just off Interstate 80, between Auburn and Sacramento, is noted for the fine specimens of agate, jasper, serpentine and soapstone that can be found there. This is not an easy place to search, however, since the lake is so large, and commercially developed in many places. It takes time and patience to properly explore this locality.

The collectibles are found scattered randomly throughout the beaches and surrounding terrain. Just walk along any shoreline and keep an eye out for the colorful jasper and white appearing agates. The best collecting is done when the lake is low, but you obviously can't plan your trip around a local drought. If you have little or no luck at one place, just hike or drive to yet another spot and try again. It seems that access from the Auburn side, to the northeast, is less developed and affords the best collecting.

The soapstone and serpentine can also be found along the shore, but better and larger pieces can be picked up in the nearby hills and canyons. Just be patient, enjoy the scenic lake, and this trip can be rewarding.

While in the area, be sure to visit Sacramento, the Capitol of California. There are many historical sites there, most notably, Old Sacramento and the Capitol Building.

Auburn was one of the original mining towns of the Mother Lode, due to gold being discovered there in 1848. It is a beautiful town, with many remnants from its glory days. Be sure to visit the magnificent Placer County Courthouse, Old Auburn, and the town museum, all very helpful in providing better insight into the rich mining history which helps make this such an interesting place to visit.

FOLSOM LAKE

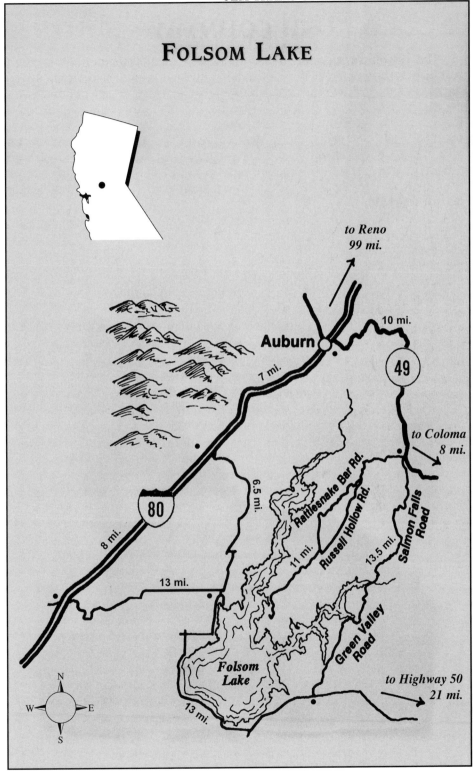

to Reno
99 mi.

10 mi.

Auburn

7 mi.

49

to Coloma
8 mi.

Rattlesnake Bar Rd.

6.5 mi.

Russell Hollow Rd.

Salmon Falls Road

80

11 mi.

13.5 mi.

8 mi.

13 mi.

Green Valley Road

Folsom Lake

to Highway 50
21 mi.

N
W   E
S

13 mi.

GOLD RUSH COUNTRY - SOUTH

This is actually a continuation of Site #50, but, this time, examining the southern portion of Gold Rush Country. As in the northern Gold Rush Country, the old dumps and surrounding countryside offer collectors an unlimited variety of minerals, including agate, jasper, marble, opal, fossils, serpentine, gold, garnet, pyrite, chalcopyrite, mica, mariposite, jade, epidote, vesuvianite, quartz crystals, and much more. Most of the dumps scattered throughout this area may have been abandoned for nearly a century, but they are probably still privately owned. It is therefore necessary to inquire in towns near any site you want to explore for ownership information **before** collecting, and by all means, **do not trespass**.

Placerville, or "Hangtown" served as the transportation center for much of the region during the gold rush. It lies in what was an extensive mining locality and affords numerous opportunities for picture taking. Be sure to see the 1800's architecture, City Hall, and the El Dorado County Museum, at the Fairgrounds. **Mokelumne Hill** boasts the old Leger Hotel, built in the mid-1850's and still open. In addition, much of the town still looks as it did over one hundred years ago.

In **Volcano**, be sure to see the still operating St. George Hotel, the turn of the century Jail, and the old printing office. **Indian Grinding Rocks State Historic Park** is also worth the visit. **Angels Camp** boasts lots of historical sites and an interesting museum. Nearby **Murphys** is regarded as one of the most picturesque of the gold rush towns, and walking down Main Street, it is like taking a walk back in time. **Columbia State Historical Park** is probably the best preserved of all the Gold Rush towns. There are two museums, lots of restored buildings, a magnificent hotel, and numerous shops and restaurants. **Copperopolis** is noted, not for gold, but for the rich copper deposits found nearby. Many old buildings remain there as does an interesting Gold Rush era cemetery. At **Knights Ferry**, you can see one of the very few remaining covered bridges in the state.

Murphys – a typical Gold Rush town

GOLD RUSH COUNTRY - SOUTH

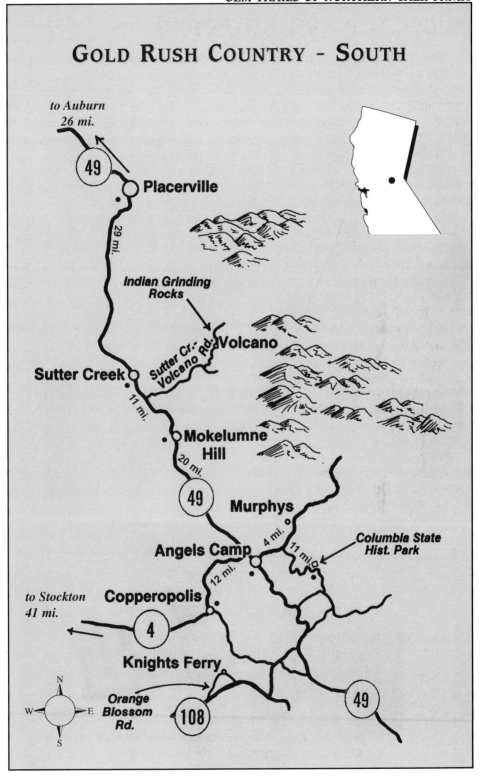

to Auburn
26 mi.

49

Placerville

29 mi.

Indian Grinding
Rocks

Sutter Cr.-
Volcano Rd.

Volcano

Sutter Creek

11 mi.

Mokelumne
Hill

20 mi.

49

Murphys

4 mi.

11 mi.

Columbia State
Hist. Park

Angels Camp

12 mi.

to Stockton
41 mi.

Copperopolis

4

Knights Ferry

49

N
W — E
S

Orange
Blossom
Rd.

108

49

BEAR RIVER

Nice pink feldspar can be gathered on the cliffs in and around the quarry shown on the accompanying map. The property is owned by the Pacific Gas and Electric Company (PG&E) and permission **MUST** be obtained before you commence collecting. You can get permission by either calling (800) 743-5000 before your visit, or by asking any of the employees working in or around the lake. No mining is done there anymore, but the quarry interior serves as a good place for the electric company to store poles and heavy equipment.

To get there, take Highway 88 east from Jackson 38.3 miles and turn right toward the Bear River Reservoir. Proceed another 2.3 miles and the quarry will be easily spotted, on the right, just before you cross the dam. After going two miles, there is a left turn to the Lodge, but you bear straight ahead.

Be very careful if you choose to do any climbing on or around the quarry walls, since a lot of the rock is loose. Do not do any heavy sledge work directly under precarious overhangs, since large boulders could easily become dislodged and create an extreme hazard to you and others nearby. The most productive method for gathering nice examples of feldspar crystallization is not to attack the quarry wall, but to simply examine the rubble scattered below for crystal bearing boulders. Use a rock pick, hand sledge, chisel, and possibly some gads to either remove the feldspar or a portion of rock containing the crystallization.

Small pyrite crystals can also be found throughout the quarry and in much of the rock along Bear River, below the dam. Split any suspect stones in hopes of exposing the glistening, golden cubic crystals. If you decide to explore the riverbanks, be advised that it is a very steep and potentially hazardous climb down. Use good judgment and don't do anything you may not be physically capable of. Following the road as it winds down and then hiking back is probably the best way to access the river.

There is a forest service campground beyond the dam if you wish to spend the night in the area, and the reservoir offers good fishing.

The quarry at the center of the Bear River site

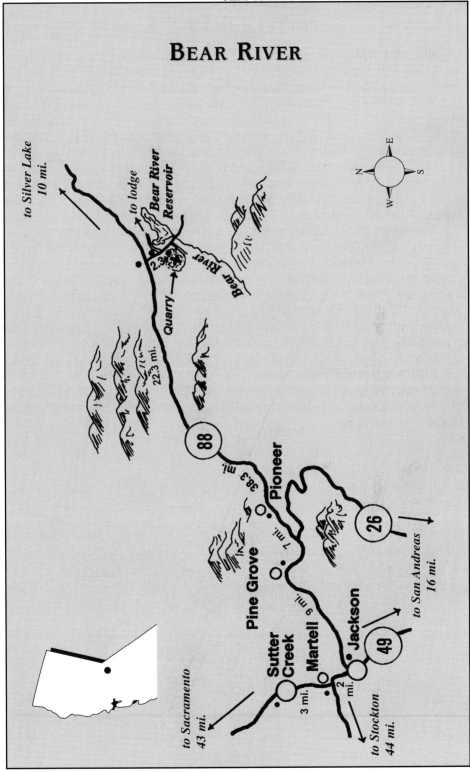

BEAR RIVER

to Silver Lake 10 mi.

to lodge

Bear River Reservoir

2.3 mi.

Quarry

Bear River

22.3 mi.

88

38.3 mi.

Pioneer

26

to San Andreas 16 mi.

7 mi.

Pine Grove

9 mi.

Sutter Creek

Martell

Jackson

49

3 mi.

2 mi.

to Sacramento 43 mi.

to Stockton 44 mi.

MOUNT REBA

There are a number of fossil deposits throughout the region surrounding Mt. Reba, about 53 miles east of Angels Camp, but most are very difficult to reach. This location is relatively easy to get to, but four-wheel drive might be needed if the roads are wet or have become washed out. In addition, it is definitely **not** a winter trip. Save it for the summer, late spring or early fall. Be advised that the Forest Service has restrictions related to fossil collecting and you should inquire at any Stanislaus National Forest office for further details.

The trip starts in Bear Valley, which is on Highway 4 approximately 46 miles east of Angels Camp. From town, go east 2.2 miles and turn left onto Highway 207, heading toward Mt. Reba and the Bear Valley Ski Area. After having gone only one mile, proceed right onto Lake Valley Road, continuing 2.5 more miles. This stretch *may* be too rough for passenger cars, so use good judgment. At the given mileage, tracks can be seen leading up the hill to the right. Follow them about 0.1 miles farther and park on the ridge. If you have doubts about making the climb, stop down below and hike up.

From the ridge, follow what was once the road toward Underwood Valley. The 17 million-year-old fossils are embedded in the yellowish to greenish sandstone on the left-hand roadcut. Break out a chunk, split it, and search for traces of ancient leaves and twigs. Be very careful when you do discover something. It takes considerable patience with a small sharp knife and/or awl to gently break away overlying host rock to display complete fossils.

Occasional pieces of petrified wood can be found on the opposite side of the old road. Look throughout the slopes to the right, and you may find some good specimens.

MOUNT REBA

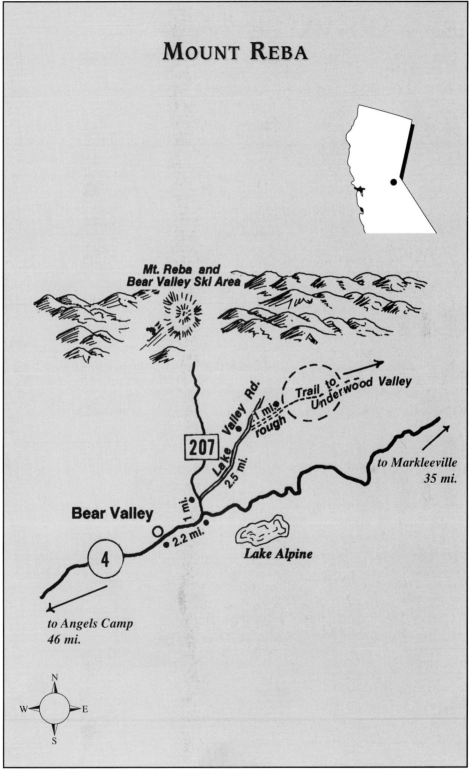

Mt. Reba and
Bear Valley Ski Area

Lake Valley Rd.

Trail to
Underwood Valley

1 mi.

rough

207

2.5 mi.

to Markleeville
35 mi.

Bear Valley

1 mi.

2.2 mi.

4

Lake Alpine

to Angels Camp
46 mi.

N
W   E
S

VALLEY SPRINGS

Valley Springs is noted throughout California for the fine minerals which can be found throughout a vast area surrounding the town. The region offers, among other things, dendritic and moss agate, spectacular blue and red agate, jasper, colorful common moss opal, jade, serpentine, soapstone, and even some gold. The problem with trying to collect here, however, is that virtually all the land is privately owned. At one time, local ranchers allowed rockhounds onto their property, but, over the years, their generosity was abused and insurance rates became prohibitive. Now there is only one reliable place still available, that being the Snyder Ranch, just north of town. Be advised, however, that the ranch is only open to rockhounds the **first weekend in May** during the annual Valley Springs Pow Wow.

During the Pow Wow, local collectors will be available to help you find exactly what you are looking for. Since time is so limited and since different minerals tend to be in different parts of the ranch, this is definitely most helpful. In some places material is scattered on the ground and in others it is necessary to use hard rock tools such as gads, chisels and a hand sledge to break away specimens. Beyond exploring the renowned Snyder Ranch, additional guided field trips to other locations are offered to attendees. It is a great opportunity to get together and share ideas with other rockhounds and, at the same time, be able to get a good variety of outstanding minerals. For more information, contact the Valley Springs Chamber of Commerce (209) 772-3245.

Valley Springs Pow Wow site

VALLEY SPRINGS

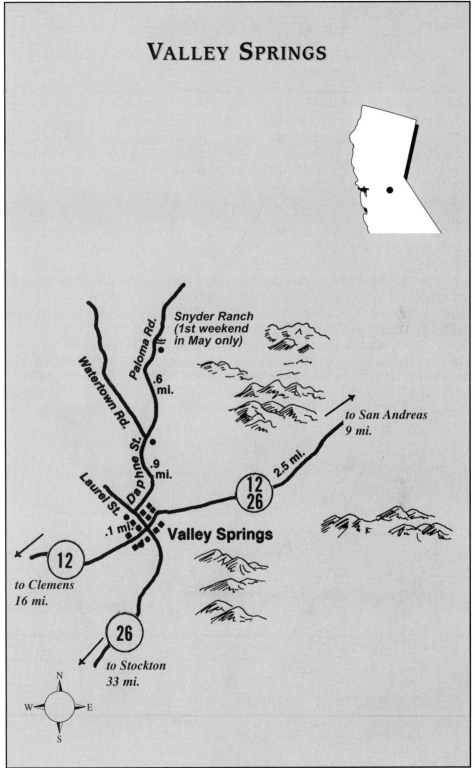

BRIDGEPORT

There are countless mines nestled in the hills and valleys to the east and northeast of Bridgeport, some of which are abandoned and offer collectors a variety of nice mineral specimens. The major difficulty with collecting in this area, however, is that the ownership status of those mines changes frequently. One that was abandoned last week may now be reactivated and vice versa. The local mining history is centered around gold and silver, primarily gold, but what most collectors find are good specimens of pyrite, chalcopyrite, quartz crystals, and a variety of other secondary minerals.

This is an interesting place to explore, but it does get very hot during the summer, making this trip better suited for the spring or fall. To get to the primary access road, go 3.8 miles north from Bridgeport, on Highway 182, to where Forest Road 046 intersects on the right. The turnoff is ***not marked*** until you actually get into the Toiyabe National Forest, but it is well-graded and easy to spot. From there, travel as far as you desire, directing your attention to the surrounding countryside for the remnants of past mining activity. It is most important to remember that you should not collect on dumps of active mines without getting permission to do so. If a particular dump looks like it has been recently worked, drive a little farther and try again.

You will encounter countless intersecting roads and ruts as you make this trip, and any of them could lead to good collecting. Be very careful not to get disoriented if you do leave the main road. This is a remote locality, and you could have a difficult time finding your way out, if lost. It is advisable to obtain a Toiyabe National Forest map, and possibly topographic maps covering this area, to assist with your exploration.

BRIDGEPORT

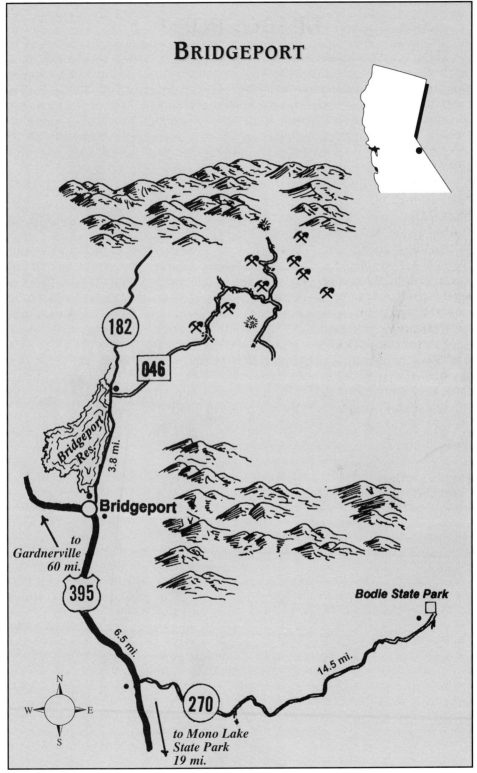

to
Gardnerville
60 mi.

Bridgeport Res.

3.8 mi.

Bridgeport

6.5 mi.

14.5 mi.

Bodie State Park

to Mono Lake
State Park
19 mi.

N
W — E
S

DILLON BEACH

Dillon Beach is situated a short distance off Highway 1, about 60 miles north of San Francisco, and is just one of many northern California beaches that offer the rockhound some nice collectibles. This particular location, and nearby Point Reyes Beach, a short distance south, provide colorful jasper and the occasional agate. Collecting is allowed at Dillon Beach, but permission should be requested from a Park Ranger before picking up anything at Point Reyes.

The agate and jasper pebbles seem to be scattered randomly all over both beaches. The little gemstones are fairly easy to spot, due to their color which contrasts against the nondescript sand and gravel of the beach itself. Some of the jasper tends to blend in, though, since abrasion has made the surface dull. To overcome this, some people actually hunt on their hands and knees. This probably won't be necessary, but it could pay off.

Beyond taking a plastic bag along with you for holding the little stones, no special equipment is needed. The tumbling size pebbles are found lying on the surface, having been washed ashore. It is usually best to hunt at low tide when more beach is exposed. The heaviest deposits of agate and jasper tend to occur after severe winter storms and their associated powerful tides. Do not venture there under such circumstances, but try to arrive at a low tide as soon afterward as possible. Another advantage to winter collecting is that fewer people will be at the beach, leaving more for the hardy few determined enough to brave the dampness and cold. If you cannot visit during the winter, there may be less material to be found, but the nice weather and beautiful surroundings will more than make up for any such mineralogical deficiency.

Be sure to also pay close attention to incoming tides to prevent getting caught in areas where you might be stranded.

DILLON BEACH

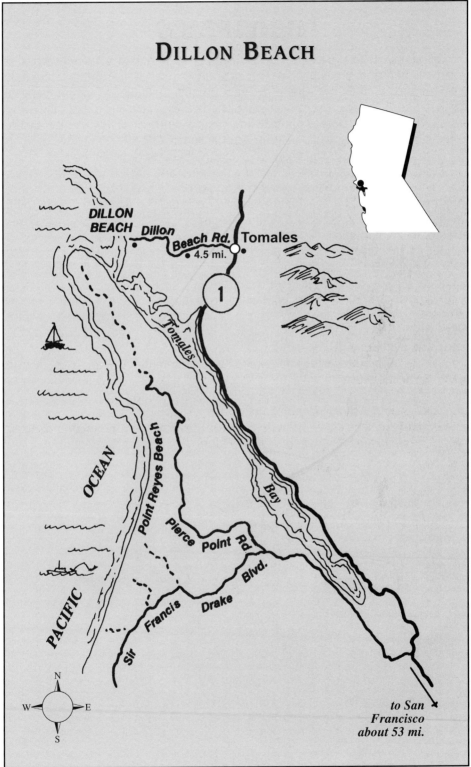

BOLINAS

Collectors can find agate and jasper pebbles scattered over many beaches in northern California, but some have considerably higher concentrations than others. One such productive location is Agate Beach, situated only a short distance north of San Francisco. To get there, take Highway 101 north about 10 miles and then turn onto Highway 1, proceeding approximately 15 more miles to the Bolinas turnoff. Agate Beach is located at the end of Elm Street, as illustrated on the accompanying map, and there is a good parking lot right there.

From the parking lot, walk along the trail about 100 yards to the shore. The agate and jasper can be found throughout the gravel for quite a distance in either direction, and specimens are easy to spot. The beach is most known for its water clear agates containing interesting, black, spot-like inclusions. That material is called "oil agate," and, if the included "blobs" are well defined, it polishes into very interesting pieces prized by collectors and lapidary craftsmen. The jasper tends to be less interesting than the oil agate, but some good color variation and patterning can be found.

The best time to hunt at this beach, as at any beach, is when the tide is receding, thereby exposing a fresh deposit of gravel. Be sure to also look for abalone shell and petrified whale bone, neither of which is as prevalent as the agate and jasper but still worth looking for.

Take a plastic bag with you for holding your finds. The agate is easy to spot, appearing white against the darker beach gravels. The jasper blends in more, however, thereby being more difficult to pick out.

This is a most scenic locality, and it doesn't take long to gather a quantity of specimens. Pay close attention to the tide. If it starts coming in, do not allow yourself to be trapped somewhere where you will not be able to get out.

Agate Beach

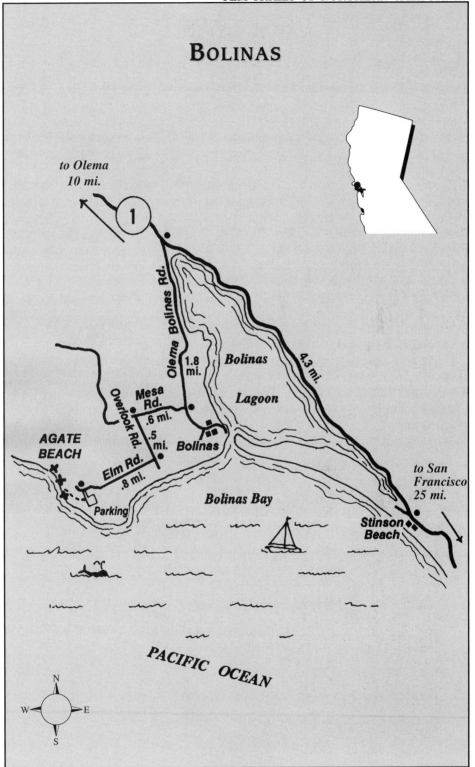

BOLINAS

to Olema
10 mi.

1

Olema Bolinas Rd.

1.8 mi.

Bolinas

Lagoon

4.3 mi.

Overlook Rd.

Mesa
Rd.

.6 mi.

.5 mi.

Bolinas

**AGATE
BEACH**

Elm Rd.

.8 mi.

Bolinas Bay

Parking

to San
Francisco
25 mi.

**Stinson
Beach**

PACIFIC OCEAN

N
W E
S

PACIFICA SOUTH

This is an extensive beach location, extending from the town of Pacifica, in the north, to Half Moon Bay, approximately 15 miles farther south. All along this coastline, rockhounds can find randomly scattered deposits of colorful jasper, agate, jade, chert, and occasional pebbles filled with little pyrite crystals. This entire stretch of beach offers lots of collecting potential, but some portions are far more accessible than others. Do not trespass onto any private areas, don't collect on any State Park Beaches, and try to visit during a low tide.

Concentrations vary greatly, and no particular spot seems to be consistently the best producer. It depends upon the tides, weather, and other factors, as to exactly where the most desirable material will be found on any given day.

Choose the spot you want to explore, take along a plastic bag for holding what you find, and start walking, examining any stones you might come upon. No special equipment is needed, since the pebbles are found lying on the surface. Once you locate samples of each of the different minerals available throughout here, subsequent pieces tend to be easier to spot. Much tends to be water worn, and when dry, has a whitish abraded surface, making identification a little tougher. Any suspect stones should be rinsed in the nearby ocean to better display color and patterning.

This is a most relaxing and scenic spot to look for rocks, and is especially desirable during the summer months when the weather is more pleasant. Winter collecting offers the greatest potential for finding larger quantities, however. Severe storms at sea cause more violent tidal forces and powerful waves, which consequently, deposit more onto the beaches. That, combined with considerably fewer people at that time of the year, tend to make it more productive.

PACIFICA SOUTH

**DO NOT COLLECT
ON STATE BEACHES !**

OCEAN

San Francisco

SAN

PACIFIC

FRANCISCO

12 mi.

4 mi.

Pacifica

280

101

BAY

Vallemar

Rockaway
Beach

San Pedro Pt.

15.5 mi.

1

about 15 mi.

*to San Mateo
Bridge*

Gray Whale St. Bch.
Montara St. Bch.

15 mi.

Montara

Moss Beach

92

Princeton
El Granada
Miramar

Half Moon

Bay Rd.

7.5 mi.

N
W — E
S

*Half Moon Bay
State Beach*

Half Moon Bay

PATTERSON

These three spots are easily accessible locations where collectors can obtain delicate little leaf fossils. To get to Site "A", follow Interstate 5 about 40 miles south from Stockton to the Patterson turnoff, Road J-17. Go west toward Lake Del Valle one mile exactly, and on the right there will be a place to pull off the pavement. Park there and inspect the bank directly across the road. The seventy million-year-old leaves and twigs are found by splitting chunks of the brownish layered shale-like sandstone. It is within the bedding planes that you will find the delicate leaves. Pay closest attention to the lighter colored, more fine-grained sections of the sedimentary formations, since these seem to contain the largest number of fossils.

It takes a great deal of care and patience to expose a complete leaf, but even partials can make outstanding display pieces. Once you discover something, be very patient, use a small, sharp knife to very carefully continue the splitting, trying to remove small amounts of the overlying sandstone at a time, without damaging the fragile fossils.

Site "B" is just 1.1 miles farther along Road J-17, and offers similar collecting. Specimens do not seem as prevalent here as at Site "A" and parking is a little tougher. Do not stop even partially on the pavement. If you must pull off a short distance away from the Site "B" roadcut, do so. This isn't a heavily traveled stretch of roadway, but occasionally a driver comes through very fast. Motorists will not be expecting to encounter stopped vehicles or pedestrians through here. Be sure to immediately remove any rock that might roll onto the pavement.

Site "C", another 0.9 miles along, is another roadcut offering yet more of the same. It is possibly a little more productive than Site "B", but Site "A" seems to be the most consistent of all. Do not be misled, however. Nothing just jumps out at you at any of the three sites. It will take some patient splitting of the sedimentary layers to locate plant remains, and immense patience, or an inordinate amount of luck, to get perfect specimens.

*A view of
Patterson Site B,
from the road*

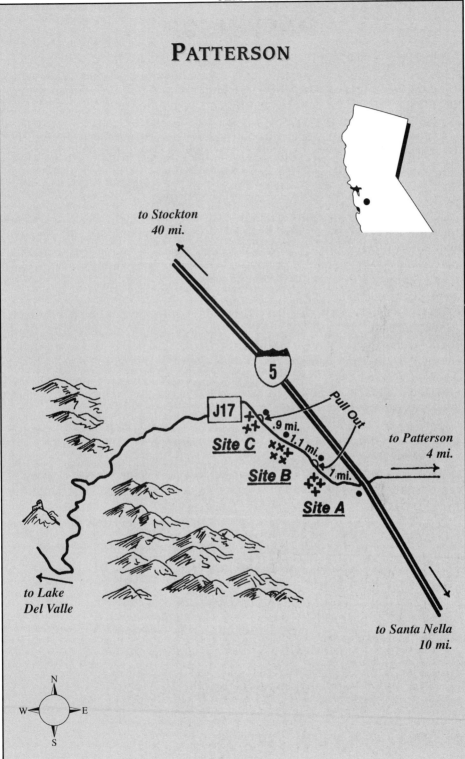

PATTERSON

to Stockton
40 mi.

5

J17

Pull Out

Site C

.9 mi.
1.1 mi.

to Patterson
4 mi.

Site B

1 mi.

Site A

to Lake
Del Valle

to Santa Nella
10 mi.

N
W E
S

ANDERSON LAKE

Blue, white and clear agate, some containing interesting moss-like inclusions, can be found along the shores of Anderson Lake, situated about 75 miles south of San Francisco. In addition, specimens of whitish to light green magnesite, in association with serpentine, can also be obtained, as can occasional pebbles of colorful jasper.

To get to Anderson Reservoir, take the Cochran exit from Highway 101, just north of Morgan Hill, as illustrated on the accompanying map. Head east, following the signs, to the lake parking area, about 2.5 miles from the freeway. Material can be found randomly scattered all along the shoreline, but a particularly good agate seam is accessed by following the little trail leading a short distance down and around the south part of the lake, as shown on the map. The magnesite is obtained by going over the dam and then hiking along the trail heading around the little hill at lake's edge. Go only a few tenths of a mile to where you should be able to see a ridge with what appears to be rust stained veins within the host rock. It is within those veins that collectors can extract the magnesite.

You will need hard rock tools if you plan to attack either the agate seams or the magnesite deposit. A hand sledge, rock pick, chisels, small gads, gloves and goggles will probably suffice. Be somewhat discrete, however, and don't take lots of tools. According to park rangers, collecting is tolerated, but not promoted. If you choose to simply pick up loose material below the deposits or along the shore, there should be no problem. Just don't do anything major. Digging big holes or massive excavation of the cliffs overlying the lake may jeopardize your collecting efforts and possibly prohibit access to future rockhounds. In fact, it might be a good idea to clarify collecting limitations with park officials before you start.

This is a pleasant place to explore, and there are numerous roads leading to different portions of Anderson Reservoir, especially farther south in Morgan Hill. East Dunne Avenue provides numerous routes to the lake. Just go east toward Henry W. Coe State Park to access southern and eastern shores.

ANDERSON LAKE

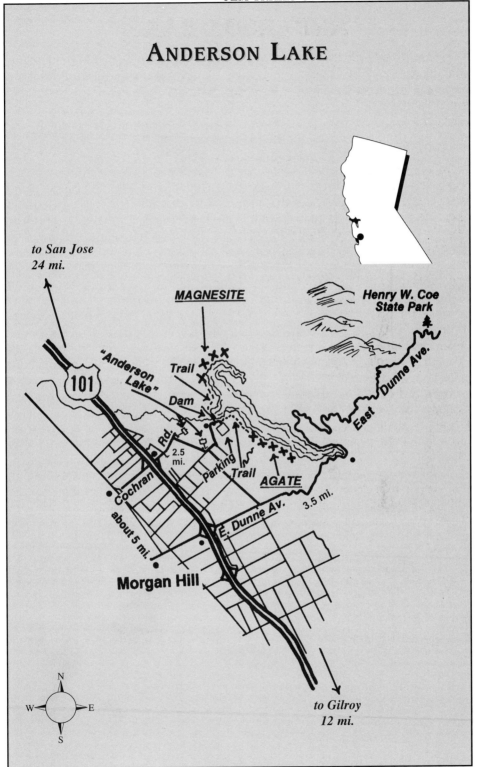

to San Jose
24 mi.

MAGNESITE

Henry W. Coe
State Park

"Anderson Lake"

101

Trail

Dam

East Dunne Ave.

Rd.

2.5 mi.

Parking

Trail

AGATE

3.5 mi.

Cochran

E. Dunne Av.

about 5 mi.

Morgan Hill

to Gilroy
12 mi.

N
W — E
S

COULTERVILLE

Beautiful green serpentine and mica-like mariposite can be found just west of Coulterville along Highway 132 and in most roadcuts on Highway 49, stretching south all the way to Mariposa. The deposits are easy to spot from a car while driving throughout the region illustrated on the map. The serpentine, especially, has a definite green to gray hue with a smooth, almost plastic-like appearance when viewed from the road. The mariposite has a more flaky texture, but the green color assists in identification.

When you find a deposit you want to examine more closely, be certain to pull completely off the pavement, since other motorists will not expect to come upon a parked car. It is necessary to use a sledge hammer, gads, and chisels to extract the finest specimens, but, if that doesn't appeal to you, there is lots of great material to be found throughout the rubble down below. If you would like to obtain better pieces of the elusive mariposite, stop by the old Harrison Mine, as shown on the map. At one time it was open, for a fee, by special appointment with the owner for amateur rockhound collecting. That status does not seem to be consistent and should be confirmed when in the area. If closed, do not trespass.

Quality of the serpentine varies considerably, with the best being bright green with tiny black stringers. Be sure, if you have the time, to inspect as many suspicious road cuts as you can, not necessarily only those shown on the map. Just be sure you do not allow rocks to get on the highway, since they can be very hazardous. In addition, do not get so excited about your excavations that you forget these are busy roadways with people traveling at high speeds. Don't get onto the pavement, and be extremely cautious if you must cross.

Additional good specimen material can also be found throughout the little hill situated about 5.2 miles north of the Merced River, as shown on the map. Just look for the ruts leading west from the highway heading toward its base.

COULTERVILLE

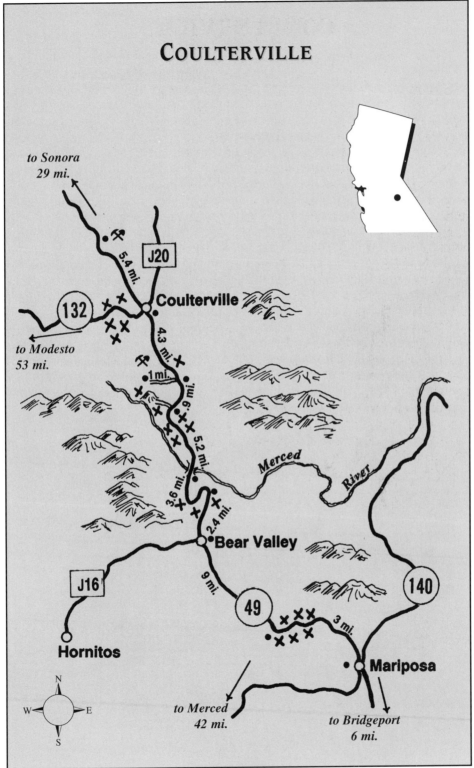

to Sonora
29 mi.

J20

132

Coulterville

to Modesto
53 mi.

5.4 mi.

4.3 mi.

1 mi.

.9 mi.

5.2 mi.

Merced
River

3.6 mi.

2.4 mi.

Bear Valley

J16

9 mi.

49

140

Hornitos

3 mi.

Mariposa

N
W   E
S

to Merced
42 mi.

to Bridgeport
6 mi.

AEOLIAN BUTTES

The eroded Aeolian Buttes, slightly visible to the east of Highway 395, about seven miles south of Lee Vining, were formed 700,000 years ago during a massive volcanic explosion that formed most of this valley. Much of the terrain between Highway 395 and those distant craters is covered with good quality obsidian. Most is deep black, but occasionally some rainbow material can be found. There are two primary roads exiting the highway into the region, and both are illustrated on the map. Go east on either and look for telltale black rock and pebbles just about anywhere between the highway and the craters. The terrain is randomly littered with obsidian, some places being completely void, while other places are covered with good quantities. It just takes some patient searching. There is also lots of pumice throughout here, and, from a distance, it is impossible to ascertain whether black rock is pumice or obsidian so you will have to investigate all suspect areas.

Be cautioned that much of the soil throughout this region is sandy and, for that reason, four-wheel drive is probably necessary since it wouldn't be a great place to get stuck. **Do not** venture too far north toward Mono Lake, since much of that land is protected and collecting is **strictly prohibited**. Be sure to stay on established roads, since there are restrictions governing off-road travel. If you spot an area of interest off the road, it will be necessary to park as close as you can get and hike the rest of the way. This is a fascinating and scenic area to see and it is recommended that you also visit Mono Lake, just north of Lee Vining, where you can get information about all of the other interesting geological sites in the area.

A view of the Aeolian Buttes from the collecting area

AEOLIAN BUTTES

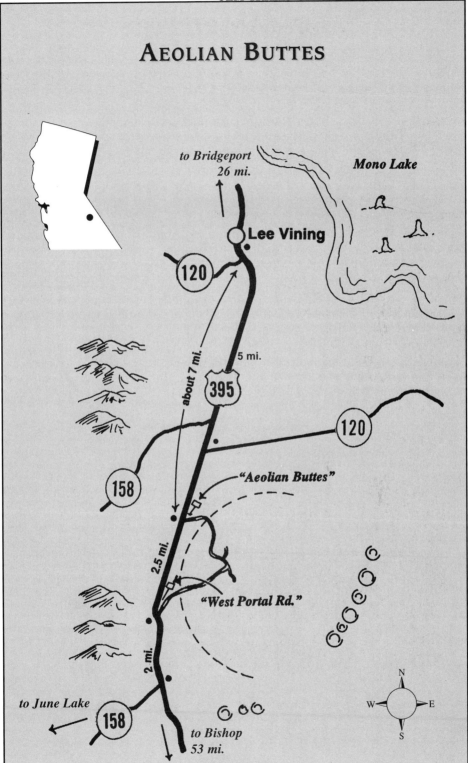

to Bridgeport
26 mi.

Mono Lake

Lee Vining

120

5 mi.

about 7 mi.

395

120

158

"Aeolian Buttes"

2.5 mi.

"West Portal Rd."

2 mi.

to June Lake

158

to Bishop
53 mi.

N
W   E
S

OBSIDIAN DOME

Obsidian can be found throughout the Mammoth Lakes / Mono Lake Region. Some specimens, as you might expect, are of a much better quality than others, and it takes some patience and a willingness to explore as much of the area as possible to find the best it has to offer. One productive and geologically interesting locality is the terrain surrounding Obsidian Dome, near Lee Vining. To get there, go south from town on Highway 395 15.2 miles to Glass Flow Road. Turn west onto this well-graded roadway and continue 1.5 miles to the dome. This is an interesting place, since it is possible to see where the obsidian actually oozed out from the crater approximately 700 years ago.

As mentioned earlier, the quality of what can be picked up here varies from near worthless opaque boulders to some that is a clear, jet black, faceting grade volcanic glass. Be advised that there are certain restrictions related to collecting obsidian in the Inyo National Forest, and it wouldn't be a bad idea to check with a Ranger at any National Forest office for further details. At time of publication, limited amounts could be picked up, but full-fledged excavations or other destructive activities were strictly prohibited. This is a most scenic region, and it would be a shame to destroy any part of the geology. Please limit your collecting to loose pieces.

Be sure, while in the area, to visit nearby Devils Punchbowl, Panum Crater, Mono Lake and, if you have the time, Devils Postpile National Monument. Even if you do not gather any obsidian, a visit to these fascinating geological sites should make it a most worthwhile trip.

Obsidian Dome (Courtesy U.S. Geological Survey)

OBSIDIAN DOME

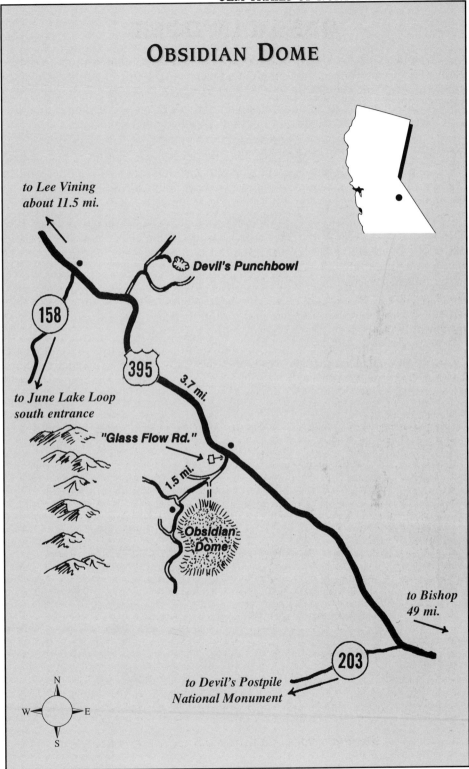

to Lee Vining
about 11.5 mi.

Devil's Punchbowl

158

395

3.7 mi.

to June Lake Loop
south entrance

"Glass Flow Rd."

1.5 mi.

Obsidian
Dome

to Bishop
49 mi.

203

to Devil's Postpile
National Monument

N
W E
S

BASALT JASPER

Colorful jasper, obsidian, petrified wood and occasional chunks of interesting agate can be found in a hidden canyon just south of Highway 6 near what was once the small town of Basalt, Nevada. This location is accessible only with four-wheel drive and the trip should not be attempted with any other type of vehicles since this would be a most inhospitable place to get stuck.

To get there, go east on Highway 6 for 1.7 miles from where Highway 360 intersects and follow the faint ruts heading south over the hill. Follow those tracks 0.8 miles, drop into the sandy wash, turn left, proceed about 0.3 miles farther and stop. From there, explore the wash and surrounding hillsides as far as you want to roam, but do not lose track of where you parked.

A bridge will be encountered about 0.2 miles farther down the arroyo, this is a remnant of the old highway which is now completely abandoned. Good material, some quite sizable, can be found on the adjacent hillsides south of that crumbling stretch of pavement and throughout the hills surrounding the wash for quite a distance in any direction, but most of the easily accessible surface material has already been picked up by previous rockhounds. For that reason, it takes more effort and hiking to gather acceptable quantities of the nice cutting materials that once littered this landscape.

The jasper is generally solid and capable of taking a good polish but some is pitted and/or porous, so be sure to gather only the best available. Colors include bright yellow and red. Occasionally chunks display many hues in a variety of patterns. The agate is more scarce, but much is filled with interesting inclusions which help to produce pleasing polished pieces. Petrified wood can also be found on some of the surrounding slopes, but it tends to be somewhat colorless and porous, consequently being suitable only for display as unpolished specimens.

Parked in sandy wash running through the Basalt location

BASALT JASPER

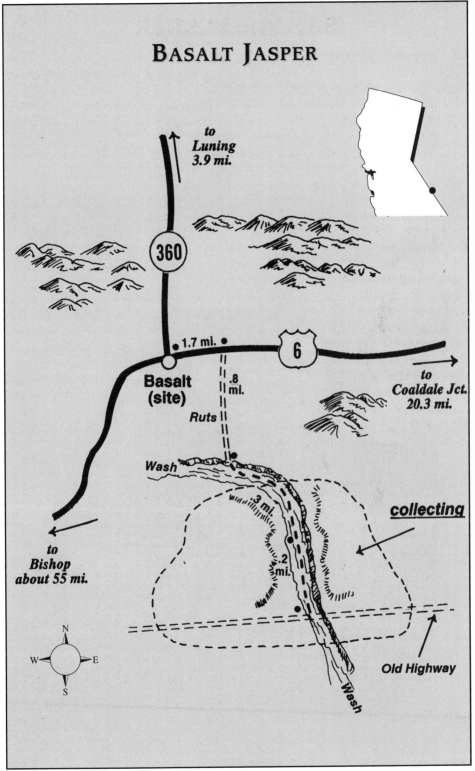

to
Luning
3.9 mi.

360

1.7 mi.

6

Basalt
(site)

.8
mi.

Ruts

to
Coaldale Jct.
20.3 mi.

Wash

.3 mi.

collecting

.2
mi.

to
Bishop
about 55 mi.

Old Highway

Wash

N
W   E
S

FISH LAKE VALLEY

Fish Lake Valley offers rockhounds lots of Apache tears, some of which can be faceted for use in jewelry. To get to this scenic location from Coaldale Junction, Nevada, take Highway 6 west 6.2 miles, and then turn south onto Highway 264. Go only 0.2 miles and then bear left onto the dirt road branching off. Continue 4.7 miles to a major fork, that marks the start of the collecting area.

From the given mileage, and continuing at least five more miles southward, one can gather countless Apache tears. The concentration varies from spot to spot, but they seem to be just about everywhere. It is helpful to keep the sun behind you when looking, since such lighting normally causes the little gems to sparkle in the soil, making the search much simpler.

Sizes vary from quite small to those measuring up to an inch in diameter. The color is predominantly jet black, but a few specimens are banded mahogany or rich brown. The terrain is flat, and the scenery is pleasant with a reed filled marsh to the south and the north.

At the south boundary of the site, which is about 10 miles from where you first started in on the dirt road, are some shallow hills. In those hills jasper and agate can be found as well as more Apache tears. The material isn't overly plentiful, but there should be enough to make it worth the extra mileage. Be sure to take time to explore that region also. The agate and jasper seem to be concentrated in certain spots and virtually void in others, so, once you locate one piece, more is often nearby.

Parked along the road leading through Fish Lake Valley

FISH LAKE VALLEY

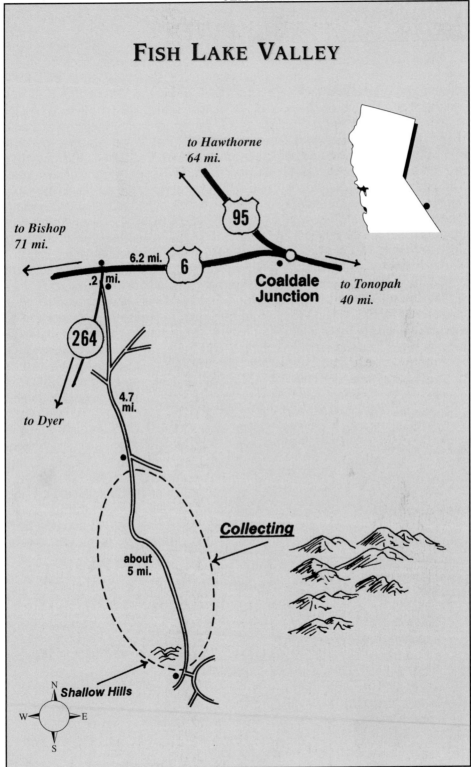

to Hawthorne
64 mi.

95

to Bishop
71 mi.

6.2 mi. **6**

.2 mi.

264

Coaldale
Junction

to Tonopah
40 mi.

to Dyer

4.7
mi.

Collecting

about
5 mi.

Shallow Hills

N
W — E
S

BIG PINE

This little collecting site is only a short distance off a paved highway making it easily accessible to most rockhounds and a great place to find well-formed smoky quartz crystals. To get there from Big Pine, go east on Highway 168, which intersects Highway 395 just north of town. The climb to Westgard Pass is very steep, making it difficult for trailers or large motor homes. It is therefore strongly suggested, even though the road is paved, that you only proceed if your vehicle has sufficient power to endure steep climbs and tight turns. The turnoff to the smoky quartz bearing hill is encountered 12.4 miles past the turnoff to the Bristle Cone Pine Forest, and, if you reach the Deep Springs Highway Maintenance Station, you have gone too far and should double back 2.2 miles. The tracks to the collecting site parallel a range fence as they lead off the pavement, and it requires some concentration to spot the turnoff. The crystal bearing hill is about 0.7 miles off the highway.

Park near the hill and either sift and rake through the soil at it's base, or use hard rock tools to follow seams and cavities within the mountain itself. Many of those voids do contain the black crystals which are often embedded in a cavity filling clay. Color ranges from light gray to jet black, and sizes can be found from small to many inches in length. By searching through and screening the low-lying soil, rockhounds can sometimes find loose crystals which have been weathered out of the rock, but, by far, the most productive method for finding the best specimens is to work on the hill. You must have a pair of gloves, sledge hammer, gads, chisels, lots of energy, and immense patience, since this is very hard labor and there are no guarantees you will open a gem

cavity. Find what appears to be a promising location using past rockhound's work areas for clues, and proceed. When you do come upon a cavity, try not to damage any crystals that may be inside. Stuffing paper into the voids will sometimes help. Most contain crystals, but, again, there are no guarantees.

Parked below the crystal bearing hill at Big Pine

BIG PINE

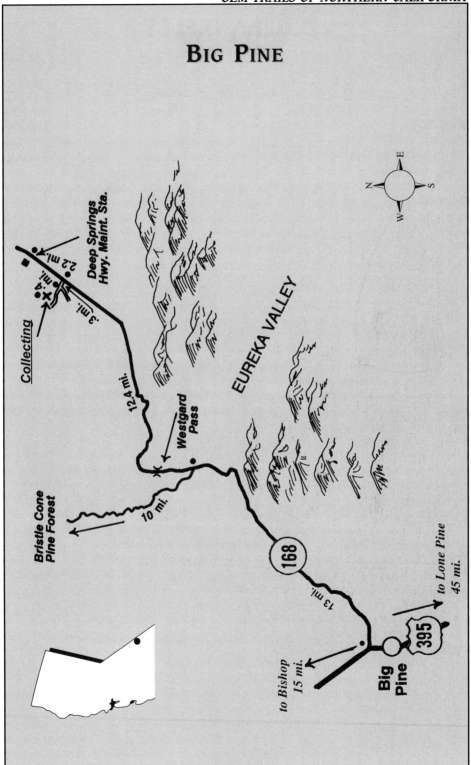

EUREKA VALLEY

Getting to this location will take you through some remote areas encompassing a variety of landscapes. It is a desolate region that gets very hot during the summer and quite cold in the winter, thereby making this a trip best reserved for the spring or fall when temperatures are less extreme. The final goal is an obsidian field where you can pick up nice black specimens of that volcanic form of glass, and maybe even stumble upon an ancient arrowhead. Do not attempt this trip unless you have plenty of supplies and a dependable, rugged vehicle.

To get to the primary collecting area, start by heading northeast on Highway 168, which intersects Highway 395 just north of Big Pine. Go 2.2 miles and then turn right onto Death Valley Road. After having gone about 15 miles, Waucoba Saline Road intersects from the south, but you should continue on Death Valley Road another 25.5 miles. As you go, there will be a number of old mines visible in the hills, any of which offer potential mineral specimens. If you have time and the access roads are not severely washed out, you might be rewarded with a variety of minerals by looking through a few of their dumps. Just be careful and don't trespass on active claims.

At the given mileage, turn right onto the dirt road and go another 10.5 additional miles, as illustrated in the map. At the edge of the sand dunes are some tracks leading off to the right and it is along that little road where you can find the obsidian.

Roam around this vast area looking for black rocks, most of which will be volcanic glass. Most is not of top quality but some is very clear and desirable for use in lapidary applications.

EUREKA VALLEY

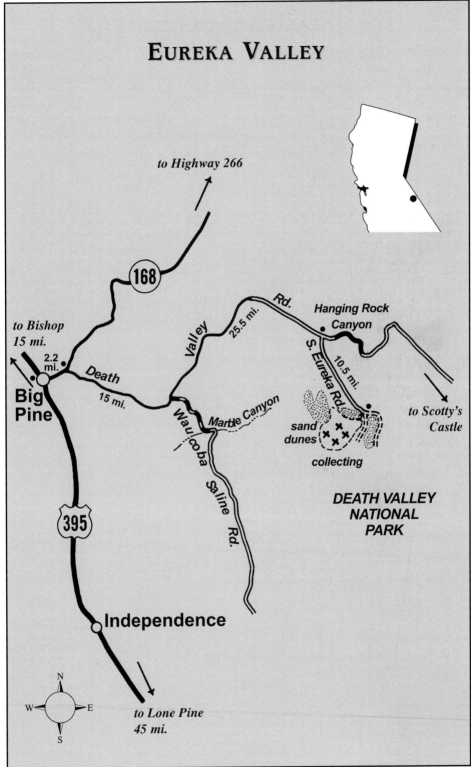

to Highway 266

168

to Bishop
15 mi.

2.2 mi.

Big Pine

Death

15 mi.

Valley

Rd.

25.5 mi.

Hanging Rock Canyon

S. Eureka Rd.

10.5 mi.

to Scotty's Castle

Waucoba

Marble Canyon

sand dunes

collecting

Saline Rd.

395

DEATH VALLEY NATIONAL PARK

Independence

to Lone Pine
45 mi.

N
W ---- E
S

HANGING ROCK CANYON

This is not a single site, but, instead, a journey past a number of mines, some active and some abandoned. The final destination is an old sulfur prospect located near Hanging Rock Canyon, not far from Death Valley National Monument. Be advised that this is a most remote area and you should go only in a rugged, dependable vehicle. In addition, the trip is not recommended during the sweltering summer months or the frigid cold of winter. Visit when your chance for pleasant weather is the greatest, either late spring or early fall. Take some extra water and supplies since you will be gone for most of a day or longer and nothing is available along the way.

Go east from Big Pine 2.2 miles on Highway 168, and then fork right onto Death Valley Road. From that point, follow the main road about 15 miles to where Waucoba Saline Road intersects. If you go right 7.5 miles on that dirt road you will be in Marble Canyon, where some interestingly banded travertine can occasionally be found among the rubble on the canyon floor on either side of the road. The main road veers left through the eastern part of Marble Canyon, but the best collecting seems to be in the more rugged western areas. If you continue east another 1.2 miles, Opal Canyon intersects on the right. As the name implies, common opal in a variety of pastel colors can be found randomly scattered throughout the canyon. In both Marble Canyon and Opal Canyon there are no specific places to collect, just search the lower areas and look for minerals of interest. Primary deposits are generally in difficult to access canyon walls and require lots of hard sledge hammer, gad and chisel work to remove specimens from the host rock.

Back on Death Valley Road, proceed approximately 33 more miles and, just before entering Hanging Rock Canyon, on your right, is the old abandoned sulfur mine. Good, yellow specimens can be found throughout the dumps. Remember – if any of the mines you visit appear to be active, respect the rights of the claimholders and do not collect there.

HANGING ROCK CANYON

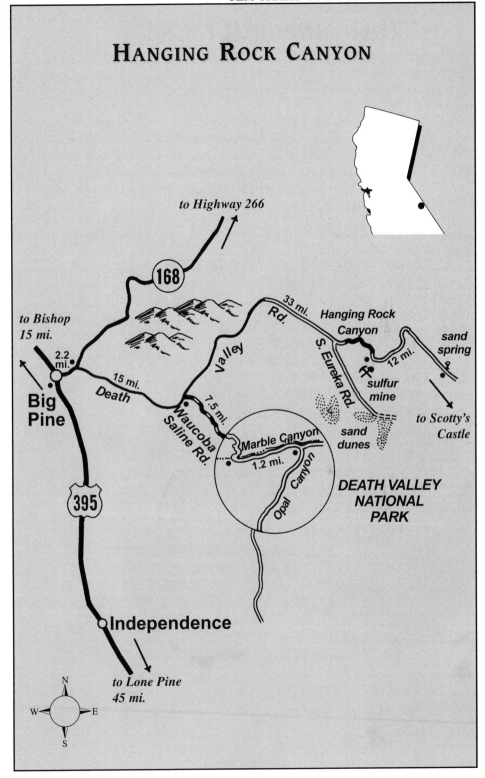

to Highway 266

168

to Bishop
15 mi.

2.2
mi.

15 mi.

Death

Valley Rd.

33 mi.

Hanging Rock
Canyon

S. Eureka Rd.

sulfur
mine

12 mi.

sand
spring

to Scotty's
Castle

**Big
Pine**

7.5 mi.

Waucoba
Saline Rd.

Marble Canyon

1.2 mi.

Opal Canyon

sand
dunes

**DEATH VALLEY
NATIONAL
PARK**

395

Independence

to Lone Pine
45 mi.

N
W E
S

WESTGARD PASS

The drive through Westgard pass is spectacular, especially near the summit as you travel through the spectacular shale deposits. It is interesting to see how the layers have been so radically altered, with the ancient bedding planes, in some places, being nearly vertical. Not only is the region scenic, but lots of fossils can be found within those spectacular cliffs, some being quite rare.

To get to the start of this somewhat extensive location, go east on Highway 168 about 11 miles from Big Pine. The road up to Westgard Pass is **very** steep and it would be most difficult if towing a trailer or driving a large motor home. It is strongly advised, even though the road is paved, that you proceed only if your vehicle has good power and can climb steep grades. In addition, for the trip back, be certain your brakes are in good condition. Their aren't many good places to turn around once you start, so if you decide to make the trip, you are fairly committed.

It is difficult to exactly pinpoint where to collect, since there are possibilities in just about all of the limestone, shale and quartzite, even though the limestone tends to be the most consistent producer. As in any such location, it just takes lots of patience and some intuition. Park in a safe location well off the pavement anywhere from where the shale and limestone starts all the way to the flats about one mile beyond the turnoff to Bristlecone Forest.

Search the white to orangish limestone for fossilized plants, most notably now extinct archaeocyathids. The shale provides trilobite specimens as well as interesting worm trails. The trilobites are few and far between, and complete examples are very difficult to obtain. Split some of the shale, though, maybe you will be lucky. The worm trails, on the other hand, are much easier to find, often completely covering a layer of the shale with countless overlapping and intersecting "grooves" left so many eons ago when this was just mud.

Most of the limestone, quartzite and shale offers collecting potential, all the way to the areas around the campground, past the summit, so be sure to try

your luck as often as you have time for. Check at the Bishop Ranger Station for complete details about restrictions related to gathering fossils in the Inyo National Forest.

The road leading through Westgard Pass

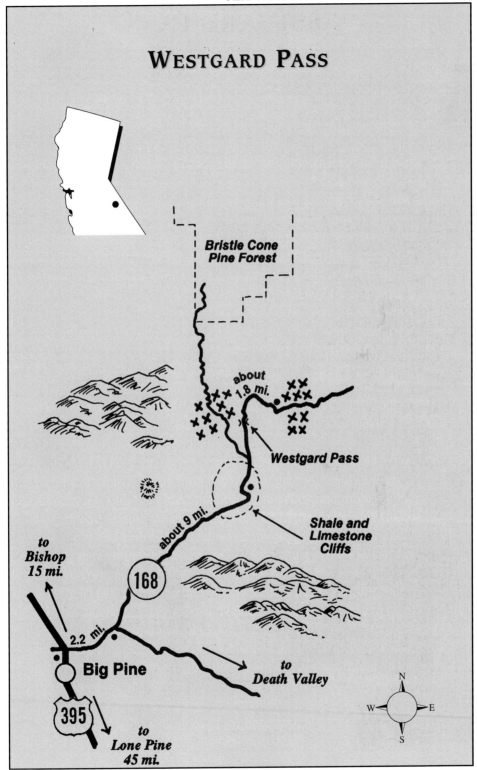

WESTGARD PASS

Bristle Cone
Pine Forest

about
1.8 mi.

Westgard Pass

about 9 mi.

Shale and
Limestone
Cliffs

to
Bishop
15 mi.

168

2.2 mi.

Big Pine

to
Death Valley

395

to
Lone Pine
45 mi.

OWENS VALLEY

Nice quartz crystals can be found at the primary collecting spot labeled Site "A" and tiny Apache tears are randomly scattered along the road shown on the map as Site "B". These places are not the only areas of interest to rockhounds in and around this highly productive ridge, and similar deposits can be found for quite a distance, stretching either north or south.

To get to Site "A", and the "gateway" to the collecting, head northeast from Highway 395 on Black Rock Fish Hatchery Road for 0.7 miles and then turn right, going off the pavement, and proceed another 4.3 miles, as shown on the map. The quartz bearing seams are situated in the hard native rock adjacent the road. Look for excavations left by previous rockhounds for ideas as to where you should start. The primary seams extend about one-half mile along the hills to the east of the road, but there are others farther in.

You can search in two different ways. The simplest is to closely examine the loose soil and rubble directly below the diggings, as well as in the flatlands farther below. A screen is most helpful for sifting through large quantities of soil in a relatively short amount of time. Just keep your eye out for the perfectly formed crystals, and you will surely find a few. Most are clear, but some are smoky. The most productive way to work this area is to attack the seams and cavities with a sledge hammer, gads and chisels, in an effort to open them and thereby provide direct access to the included crystals. This involves very hard work, but if you do open a good cavity, the rewards can be substantial.

As the main road heads north toward the ruins of Aberdeen Station it cuts through some areas of conspicuous white soil. Throughout those rather condensed whitish locations are scattered countless tiny Apache tears. Most are very nice, occurring in shades of black, mahogany, and brown. They are great for tumbling and some are even clear enough to facet. Be sure to stop and inspect a few of those spots.

Road leading through Owens Valley, Site B

OWENS VALLEY

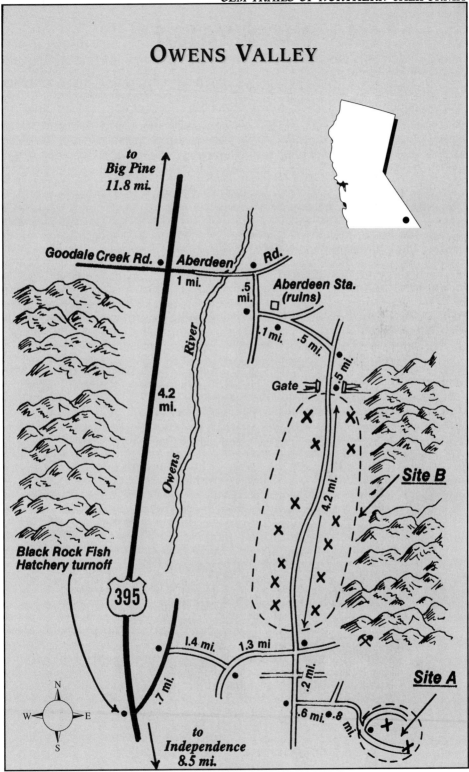

to
Big Pine
11.8 mi.

Goodale Creek Rd. • Aberdeen Rd.
1 mi.
.5 mi.

Aberdeen Sta.
(ruins)

.1 mi. .5 mi.

.5 mi.

Gate

River

4.2 mi.

Owens

4.2 mi.

Site B

Black Rock Fish
Hatchery turnoff

395

1.4 mi. 1.3 mi

.7 mi.

.2 mi.

.6 mi. .8 mi.

Site A

N
W   E
S

to
Independence
8.5 mi.

MAZOURKA CANYON

This site offers the collector an opportunity to gather 400 million-year-old fossilized coral, crinoids, and shells. To get to the primary site, take Mazourka Canyon Road east from its intersection with Highway 395, at the southern edge of Independence. Go 6.7 miles to where the road starts going north, paralleling the eastern mountain ridge, and park off the roadway. The collecting area lies within the grayish limestone, which can be seen from the road, but it is necessary to hike to that ridge, about one-half mile away. The trek isn't too bad, but tends to be a little uphill. Do not, however, attempt it during the scorching heat of summer. Take water, a rock pick and other tools, and a sturdy bag for carrying whatever you find back to your vehicle.

The coral is a brownish hue, and thereby somewhat easy to distinguish against the much lighter host limestone. In fact, as you hike to the primary deposit, lots of the coral bearing limestone will be encountered along the way. Many collectors are so satisfied with what they pick up in the lowlands that they find no need to engage in the tough hammer work required at the deposit itself. Another benefit is that occasionally, the limestone has been partially weathered away from the harder coral, making excellent display pieces, in their found condition.

In addition to the abundant coral, rockhounds can also procure good specimens of crinoid stems and other ancient plants and algae. Some of the limestone is filled with fossils, and such pieces can be used for display in collections or just as conversation pieces. If you find an especially nice fossil-filled rock, use an awl, ice pick, and/or small knife to carefully remove as much of the covering limestone as possible, in order to better expose the fossils. With some patience and a willingness to spend some time, incredible display pieces can be made.

Hiking toward the Mazourka Canyon collecting site

MAZOURKA CANYON

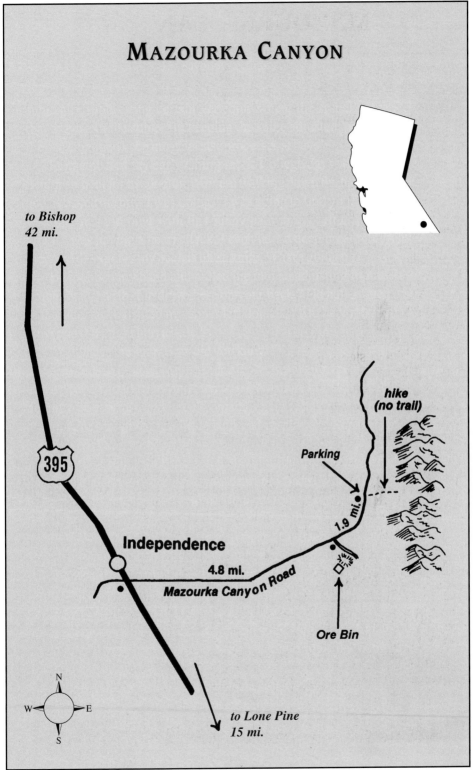

to Bishop
42 mi.

395

Independence

4.8 mi.

Mazourka Canyon Road

Parking

1.9 mi.

*hike
(no trail)*

Ore Bin

to Lone Pine
15 mi.

N
W   E
S

LONE PINE

Beautiful blue-green amazonite and an occasional beryl crystal can be found throughout the area shown in the accompanying map. The brilliant color of the amazonite makes it very easy to spot against the dull host rock, native sand, and gravel, but this is not an exceptionally productive collecting spot. Most of the specimens are quite small and strewn over a large area, but the quality of what can be found seems to make up for the scarcity.

To get to this most interesting locality, follow Highway 136 for 3.3 miles east from where it intersects Highway 395, south of Lone Pine. Go left 2.1 miles then follow the sandy tracks as they lead up to the base of the mountain, another 3.1 miles away. At that point, it gets very sandy, and four-wheel drive may be necessary. If you have any doubts about your vehicle's ability to continue, stop and hike the remaining 0.6 miles. If you can drive in, there is a sheltered box canyon at the road's end, which makes a nice place to camp if you choose to spend the night.

Look throughout the lower wash, the entire box canyon, and among the granite boulders strewn all over at road's end. If you have the energy, follow the main wash as it climbs the mountain. More amazonite can be found as you hike, and the larger and better specimens are usually discovered trapped within the stones in and around that wash. As mentioned earlier, the brilliant color makes even the smallest of chips easy to see, just pay attention as you proceed. Do not attempt the climb to the summit unless you are in good physical condition. Some of the boulders are tough to negotiate, and it would be easy to slip and fall.

If you choose to make the climb, there is a spectacular view of the Owens Valley, Lone Pine, and the mighty Sierra Nevada Mountains from the top. In fact, even if there weren't any minerals to collect, that panorama would probably make the trek worthwhile. On the summit regions, beryl and quartz crystals can sometimes be found and, at one time, there was a beryl claim up there. Do not infringe upon the claim if it appears to have been reactivated.

A view of Owens Valley from the upper portion of the Lone Pine Site

LONE PINE

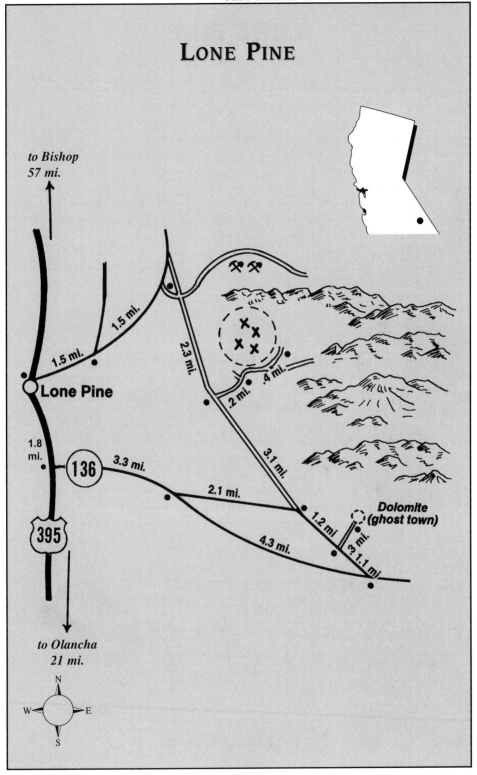

to Bishop
57 mi.

1.5 mi.

1.5 mi.

2.3 mi.

.2 mi.

.4 mi.

○ **Lone Pine**

1.8 mi.

(136)

3.3 mi.

3.1 mi.

2.1 mi.

395

Dolomite
(ghost town)

1.2 mi.

? mi.

4.3 mi.

? 1.1 mi.

to Olancha
21 mi.

N
W   E
S

COTTONWOOD LAKES

Well formed quartz and feldspar crystals are the minerals of primary interest at this collecting site, but additional more exotic minerals occur and can be found. Be advised that this is a very scenic collecting area, but should only be of interest to those with backpacking expertise and hiking equipment, since it involves a six mile uphill walk, at high altitude. In fact, the trek starts at approximately 9,500 feet and ends at New Army Pass, about 12,400 feet. Do not attempt this trek if you have any doubts about your ability. The thin air, length of hike, climb, and remoteness make it a trip only a very few rockhounds should consider!

If you are ready for the challenge, as well as an opportunity to hike through some of California's most beautiful scenery, you must first get a wilderness permit at the Ranger Station in Lone Pine. After securing the permit, head west from town on Whitney Portal Road 3.5 miles. From there, go left onto Horseshoe Meadow Road, following it as it proceeds south around the peak and then east, up and over a ridge, and finally down to road's end and the trailhead at Horseshoe Meadow parking and camping area, a total of about 16 miles. It is suggested that you spend the night at Horseshoe Meadows in order to let your body adjust to the altitude, since altitude sickness is a common hazard to backpackers in this area.

From the campground, follow Cottonwood Creek Trail approximately six miles to Cottonwood Lakes and New Army Pass. When hiking, if you become extremely tired, have headaches, or start getting a little disoriented, those are signs of altitude sickness, and it is essential that you immediately retreat back to lower elevations. Don't gamble with your health! Just before the final climb to the pass, the trail goes through a bowl shaped region, filled with glacial debris.

The crystals are found in cavities within the granite boulders lining that "glacial amphitheater." You must scramble down and inspect the vugs for crystals. You can use gads, chisels and a sledge hammer to open suspect rocks, but when doing so, be very careful not to damage any of the fragile interiors. You obviously will need some hard rock tools, but don't take too many, since they are heavy and must be packed to the pass and then all the way back to your car along with whatever you find. It is suggested that you spend at least one night camping near New Army Pass and then head back when refreshed. Again, do not attempt this trip if you are not in top physical condition!

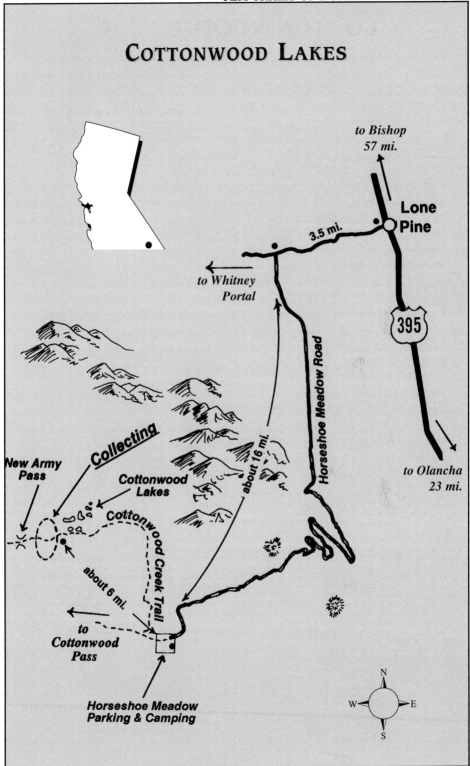

COTTONWOOD LAKES

to Bishop
57 mi.

**Lone
Pine**

3.5 mi.

to Whitney
Portal

Horseshoe Meadow Road

395

to Olancha
23 mi.

New Army
Pass

Collecting

Cottonwood
Lakes

about 16 mi.

Cottonwood Creek Trail

about 6 mi.

to
Cottonwood
Pass

**Horseshoe Meadow
Parking & Camping**

N
W   E
S

JADE COVE

Nephrite jade and actinolite specimens can be found in and below the beach cliffs along approximately two miles of coastline in the southern part of Monterey County. There are a few crude trails leading to the shore, some of which are shown on the map, but they are often steep and somewhat danger- ous. Do not climb down any bank where there is no maintained trail, or where there appears to be a hazard. The soil is unstable and continually being erod- ed away by tidal forces and severe winter storms. It is suggested that you enter from the maintained trail at the turnstile about one-quarter mile south of Plaskett Creek. Park well off the highway and be very careful when walking down. Once on the beach, if you want to explore more secluded and thereby potentially more productive areas, it will probably be necessary to scramble over large boulders along the way and possibly even do some wading. Be very careful and **DO NOT** attempt anything you are not physically capable of doing.

The jade is found as pebbles and boulders in the cliffs themselves, as well as lying along the beach. Heavy digging equipment is not needed, but a small rake and trowel are handy. Most specimens are not of translucent gem quali- ty, but there is a great deal of good green material which can be used for carv- ings or cabochons. Just be patient and willing to spend some time searching. If you choose to dig into the cliffs, be certain not to dislodge soil or rock from above. In addition, **do not** be tempted to tunnel. The soil's lack of stability would make that most foolish.

Be sure to plan your visit at **LOW TIDE** when collecting is most produc- tive and more of the shoreline is accessible. It is very important, as you col- lect, that you maintain awareness of tidal changes, since you don't want to be trapped in some isolated cove when the water starts coming in. Some stretch- es of beach, in fact, become COMPLETELY covered with water at high tide.

JADE COVE

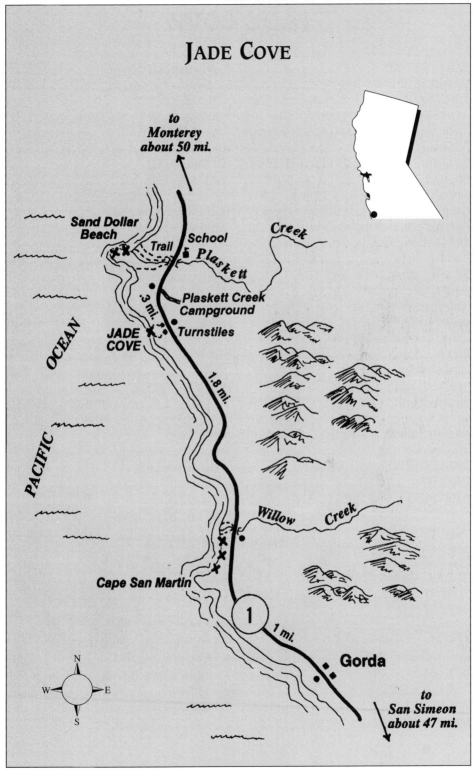

to
Monterey
about 50 mi.

Sand Dollar
Beach

Trail

School

Plaskett

Creek

Plaskett Creek
Campground

.3 mi.

JADE
COVE

Turnstiles

OCEAN

1.8 mi.

PACIFIC

Willow   Creek

Cape San Martin

1

1 mi.

Gorda

to
San Simeon
about 47 mi.

N
W   E
S

GLOSSARY

A

Agate – A banded, fine-grained or variegated chalcedony having its colors arranged in stripes, blended in clouds or showing moss-like forms.

Almandine Garnets – The common garnet, a reddish iron-alumina stone found crystallized as a rhombic dodecahedron. An inexpensive gem and an abrasive. It is sometimes called almandite.

Alder – Any of a small group of rapidly growing trees and shrubs of the birch family, having toothed leaves and catkins, and growing in cool, moist soil in temperate and cold climates.

Ammonites – Any of the flat, usually coiled fossil shells of the extinct order (Ammonoidea) of cephalopod mollusks dominant in the Mesozoic era.

Apache Tears – An obsidian nodule that has been weathered out of a lava deposit.

Arroyo – A dry gully, rivulet or stream.

Azurite – Brilliantly blue or violet monoclinic mineral that is an ore of copper.

B

Banded Agate – Agates with colors usually arranged in delicate parallel alternating bands or stripes of varying thickness. The bands are sometimes straight but usually wavy and concentric.

Basalt – The most common extrusive igneous rock or lava. Basalt is primarily composed or pyroxene and feldspar. Highly fluid basalt that quickly covers a large area is referred to as flood basalt.

Bed – The smallest layer of sedimentary rock, usually a layer from one depositional event such as a flood.

Bentonite Ash – A porous clay consisting mainly of the mineral montmorillonite, which swells greatly when it absorbs water.

Berm – The margin or shoulder of a road, adjacent to and outside the paved or graded portion.

Black Tears – A nickname for Apache tears.

Bloodstone – A green jasper spotted with red, as if with blood. Also called heliotrope.

Bogwood – Wood that was petrified after having been partially decayed due to its lengthy suspension in a lake, swamp or mud.

Brachiopod – Belonging to the phylum of marine animals with hinged upper and lower shells enclosing two armlike parts with tentacles that are used for guiding minute food particles into the mouth.

Bull's-eye Agate – Agate which displays concentric circular lines resembling a bull's-eye target when cut and polished perpendicular to the banding planes.

C

Cabochon – A gem cut style distinguished by its smooth convex top and no facets.

Calcite – A mineral consisting of calcium carbonate crystallized in hexagonal form found in common limestone, chalk and marble.

Calcite Clusters – A cluster or group of calcite crystals.

Carnelian Agate – An orange variety of agate.

Cavity – A hole or hollow place.

Chalcedony – A clear and colorless agate without patterns or inclusions. A translucent or micro-crystalline form of quartz that is often pale blue or gray with a nearly wax-like luster.

Chert – Cryptocrystalline sedimentary rock similar to flint. White, black, gray or banded chert is often found as nodules within limestone and dolomite layers.

Chrysocolla – A silicate of the protoxid of copper with a fine emerald-green color, apparently produced from the decomposition of copper ores, which it usually accompanies.

Clastic – Consisting of fragments of older rocks.

Cluster – A group of crystals growing close together.

Concretion – Spheroidal or tuberous body of mineral aggregate formed in sedimentary rocks. A hard ball or odd-shaped mass of mineral matter. Concretions form around a nucleus such as a bone, shell, leaf or fossil.

Conglomerates – A rock composed of rounded fragments of various rocks cemented together by a siliceous or other matter.

Coral – The calcareous or horny skeletal deposit produced by anthozoan or rarely hydrozoan polyps.

Crinoid Stems – The main shaft of a crinoid which attached the flower which is attached to the sea bottom.

Crinoids – A family of echinoderms surviving to the present, (commonly known as "sea lily") but often found as fossils. The stem which anchored the "flower" to the sea bottom is most often recovered.

Crystal – A homogeneous, solid body of a chemical element, compound or isomorphous mixture, having a regularly repeating atomic arrangement that may be outwardly expressed by natural planar surfaces called "faces."

Crystalline – Having the properties of a crystal; a regular internal arrangement in three dimensions of constituent atoms.

D

Decomposition – Breaking up or separating into basic components or parts.

Dendrite – A branching, treelike mark made by one mineral crystallizing in another.

Diatomite – A light-colored, soft sedimentary rock formed mainly of the siliceous shells of diatoms and used in a finely pulverized state as an abrasive, absorbent, filter, etc.

Dump – The location(s) where non-valuable discarded rock and soil are transported. Material left on the dump is regarded as too poor in quality to be of any interest to the mining process.

E

Epidote – A yellowish green mineral usually occurring in grains or columnar masses, and sometimes used as a gemstone.

Erosion – The wearing away of the earth's landscape by natural forces of water, wind, ice, waves and tides.

F

Feldspar – Any of a group of crystalline minerals that consist of aluminum silicates with either potassium, sodium, calcium or barium and that are an essential constituent of nearly all kinds of rocks.

Fissure – A narrow crack or opening of considerable length and depth.

Fluorite – A halide group mineral frequently purple, but also found green, yellow or blue in color.

Fluorite Cubes – Cubic crystals of fluorite.

Fossil – Any preserved evidence of past life.

Fusilinid – Any foraminifer belonging to the suborder Fusulinina and characterized by a multi-chambered elongate calcareous microgranular test, commonly resembling the shape of a grain of rice.

G

Galena – Native lead sulphide. An ore from which the lead of commerce, and often silver, are obtained.

Garnet – A group of minerals rich in calcium, magnesium, iron and manganese. A brittle and transparent to sub-transparent mineral having a vitreous luster, no cleavage, and occurs in a variety of colors. It occurs as an accessory mineral in a wide range of igneous rocks, but is most commonly found as distinctive crystals in metamorphic rocks. Used as a semiprecious stone and as an abrasive.

Gastropods – Any of a large class (gastropoda) of mollusks having one-piece, straight or spiral shells like snails, limpets, etc., or having no shells or greatly reduced shells, as certain slugs.

Geode – A hollow nodule of rock usually enclosing agate and crystal formations in the center.

Graders – A tractor employed to level dirt roads.

Granite – A common igneous rock, cooled from a magma body and containing visible crystals of quartz, feldspar and mica or hornblende.

Graptolite – A small marine organism belonging to the order Graptoloidea which is characterized by a cup or tube shaped exoskeleton.

Gypsum – A soft, white mineral; hydrated calcium sulfate. Commonly formed by evaporation.

H

Hardness – Resistance to scratching; measured from 1 to 10 on the Mohs scale.

I

Inclusions – Mineral crystals enclosed within a large host mineral specimen. Inclusions may also be gas bubbles or liquid-filled cavities.

J

Jasp-agate – A combination of jasper and agate in one rock.

Jasper – An opaque cryptocrystalline quartz of any of several colors, usually red, yellow or brown.

L

Limb Cast – A mold formed when quartz filled the cavities left in dried mud by decomposed limbs and twigs. The resulting cast is often an exact replica of the original.

Limestone – A sedimentary rock composed entirely or chiefly of carbonate of calcium. When containing sand or silica, it is called siliceous; containing clay, it is argillaceous; and containing carbonate of magnesium, it is dolomitic. When firm or crystalline, it is called marble.

Limonite – A general term for a group of brown, naturally occurring hydrous iron oxides.

Lower Triassic – Earlier part of the Triassic period, occurring about 225 to 190 million years ago.

M

Malachite – Native carbonate of copper. Green malachite occurs in green mammillary masses, consisting of concentric layers having a fibrous structure. It admits a high polish.

Marble – A metamorphic rock composed of re-crystallized calcite.

Mica – Any of various colored or transparent mineral silicates crystallizing in monoclinic forms that readily separate into thin leaves.

Mineral – A naturally occurring inorganic substance that is crystalline and has a composition that can be defined by a simple chemical formula.

Mollusk – A group of invertebrate animals that includes snails, clams and the nautilus.

Moonstone – A semitransparent to translucent feldspar that exhibits a bluish to milky-white pearly or opaline luster. An opalescent variety of orthoclase feldspar.

Moss Agate – A general term used in North America for any translucent chalcedony, agate, or cryptocrystalline quartz with inclusions of any color arranged in moss-like or flower-like patterns.

N

Nodule – A small rounded lump of a mineral or mineral aggregate.

O

Obsidian – A black or brown vitreous volcanic rock. It is similar to black glass and is primarily composed of silica.

Obsidianite – Another name for an Apache tear which is an obsidian nodule that has been weathered out of a lava deposit.

Onyx – Any stone exhibiting two or more layers of strongly contrasting colors, such as banded jasper or chalcedony, especially chalcedony when it is marked with white and stratified with opaque and translucent lines.

Opal – A mineral that is a hydrated amorphous silica that is softer and less dense than quartz. It typically has a definite and often marked iridescent play of colors.

Opalite – A colored occurrence of common opal.

Orthoclase – A colorless or lightly colored mineral of the alkali feldspar group.

Outcrop – Rock exposed at the surface.

P

Perlite – A volcanic glass composed of rhyolite and containing a higher amount of water than obsidian and other more recognized forms.

Permian Age – Designating or of the sixth and last geologic period of the Paleozoic era, characterized by the formation of Pangaea; glaciation in the Southern Hemisphere; development of mountains; and an increase in the diversity of land plants and animals.

Permian Gerster Formation – Formed during the Permian period of the Paleozoic era, thought to have been about 280 to 225 million years ago.

Petrification – The process of fossilization whereby organic matter is converted into a stony substance by the infiltration of water containing dissolved inorganic matter (e.g. silica, calcium carbonate) which replaces the original organic materials, sometimes retaining the structure.

Petrified Wood – Fossilized wood in which the cells of the wood have been entirely replaced by crystallized silica and thereby converted into quartz or opal.

Pit - A hole or cavity in the ground.

Plume Agate – A variety of agate with ostrich feather-like formations.

Porosity – The ratio, usually expressed as a percentage, of the volume of a material's pores, as in rock, to its total volume.

Psilomelane – A general reference to a variety of manganese minerals frequently displaying a bubbly botryoidal occurrence.

Pyrite – A common isometric mineral that consists of iron disulfide and has a pale brass-yellow color and metallic luster. Frequently crystallized and is also massive in mammillary forms with a fibrous or stalactite structure with a crystalline surface. Also known as iron

Pyrite Cubes – Pyrite in a cubic formation.

Q

Quartz – A mineral, silicon dioxide, that occurs in colorless and transparent or colored hexagonal crystals and also in crystalline masses. An important rock forming mineral.

R

Rainbow Agate – Agate that, when polished, exhibits the spectrum of the rainbow.

Rhombs – Crystals displaying a rhombohedral structure. It is a six-sided, roughly equidimensional crystal.

Rhombohedral – Designating or of a crystal system having three axes of equal length, none of which intersects at right angles with another.

Rhyolite – A group of extensive igneous rocks. A very acid volcanic rock that is the extrusive form of granite.

Rock – A consolidated assemblage of grains of one or more minerals.

Rough – The raw gemstone.

S

Sandstone – A medium grained, sedimentary rock consisting primarily of quartz grains cemented by silica, lime or iron oxide.

Scar – A precipitous rocky place or cliff.

Seam – A visible line of rock or mineral passing through a larger mass of rock, such as a seam of quartz in a limestone quarry wall.

Selenite – A variety of sulfate of lime or gypsum occurring in transparent crystals or crystalline masses.

Semiprecious Stones – Designating gems of lower value than those classified as precious. Examples are garnets and turquoise.

Shale – A fissile rock that is formed by the consolidation of clay, mud or silt and has a finely stratified or laminated structure. Composed of minerals essentially unaltered since deposition.

Silica – Silicon dioxide. A component of chert, flint, agate and quartz.

Silicified wood – A term which includes all varieties of wood that have been converted into silica.

Siltstone – A rock formed from silt that has a texture and composition of shale but lacks its lamination, sometimes referred to as mudstone. It is a rock whose composition is between sandstone and shale.

Smoky Quartz – A variety of quartz occurring in shades from gray to black.

Stringers – Thin mineral veins or filaments, usually occurring in nonparallel patterns within a host rock or mineral.

Sulfur – A pale-yellow nonmetallic chemical element found in crystalline or amorphous form.

T

Tailings – Waste or refuge piles left from various processes of milling, mining, distilling, etc.

Trapezoidal Crystals – Crystals that have have two parallel sides.

Triassic – Reference to the earliest period of the Mesozoic era of 195 to 225 million years ago, or the corresponding system of rocks.

Trilobite – Extinct Paleozoic marine arthropods having the segments of the body divided by furrows on the dorsal surface into three lobes.

Tumbling – The act of using a revolving box or drum into which loose materials are loaded and tumbled about for use in mixing or polishing.

Turquoise – A greenish-blue, hard mineral that is a hydrous copper aluminum phosphate.

U

V

Variegated – Marked with different colors in spots, streaks; partly-colored.

Variety – A named specific color or other quality of a gemstone species, such as ruby for red corundum.

Vein – A continuous body of minerals, igneous or sedimentary rock, etc. occupying a fissure of zone, differing in nature from the enclosing rock.

Volcanic Glass – Natural glass, as obsidian, formed by the very rapid cooling of molten lava.

Volcanism – The process of extruding magma, lava or ash to the earth's surface.

Vug – A cavity or hollow in a rock or lode, often lined with crystals.

W

Wash – Eroded soil that has been transported by running water. The broad, gravelly, normally dry streambed, often located at the bottom of a canyon.

Weathered – Stained, worn or beaten by the weather.

Wonderstone – A banded rhyolite.

Wood Agate – Agatized wood in which the structure of wood is plainly shown.

X

Y

Z

NOTES